Penguin Books

Makapan's Caves and Other Stories

Herman Charles Bosman was born of Afrikaner parents in the Cape Colony, South Africa, in 1905. As a young English teacher he encountered the submerged backveld world of the Transvaal in the 1920s, a devastated area still recovering from the Anglo-Boer War. Sentenced to death for murder, Bosman was reprieved in 1930. Until his death in 1951 he worked as a journalist and writer in Johannesburg and London. He published some 160 short stories, twenty-seven of which are in this selection.

During his brief career, Bosman was an assiduous chronicler of dominion South Africa, a Commonwealth writer fascinated by the interaction of metropolitan powers and small colonized populations. In the South African context he told the stories that are the common experience of many writers of 'new literature in English'. His shrewd and probing insight, his astute wit, together with his inventive use of techniques in writing short fiction, make him a popular favourite in South Africa. His satires on racial intolerance also make him one of the toughest writers to have challenged the early apartheid society.

Stephen Gray was born in Cape Town in 1941. He went to Cambridge University to complete a Masters degree in English in 1964. While at Cambridge he was editor of *Granta* for a short time. Since 1969 he has lived and worked in Johannesburg where he is Professor of English at the Rand Afrikaans University. He is a novelist and poet, has worked in the theatre and has edited several collections of South African writing, including *The Penguin Book of Southern African Stories*.

Herman Charles Bosman

Makapan's Caves and Other Stories

Edited by Stephen Gray

Penguin Books

Penguin Books Ltd, Harmondsworth, Middlesex, England
Viking Penguin Inc., 40 West 23rd Street, New York, New York 10010, U.S.A.
Penguin Books Australia Ltd, Ringwood, Victoria, Australia
Penguin Books Canada Limited, 2801 John Street, Markham, Ontario, Canada L3R 1B4
Penguin Books (N.Z.) Ltd, 182–190 Wairau Road, Auckland 10, New Zealand

This selection first published 1987

The Acknowledgements on pages 188–90 constitute an extension of this copyright page

Typeset in 9/11 Linotron Sabon by
Rowland Phototypesetting Ltd
Bury St Edmunds, Suffolk

Printed in Great Britain by Cox & Wyman Ltd, Reading

Contents

Introduction

Herman Charles Bosman was born in Kuil's River, outside Cape Town, South Africa, in 1905. His father was a white mine-worker, his mother a middle-class teacher of a good Afrikaner family. The marriage was not a success. Following his migrant parents, the young Bosman went to an Afrikaans-medium school in Potchefstroom, and then to an English-medium one in Johannesburg, where he lived most of his short life. He had an undistinguished academic career at the University of the Witwatersrand and at its Normal College where, in 1925, he qualified as a school-teacher and began publishing copiously insipid fin-de-siècle-type poems; he was an aesthetic Bohemian, briefly a Communist, certainly always a rebel – and an Afrikaner thoroughly mixed into the liberal British establishment.

His father died, and his mother remarried – this time an English-speaking mineworker with children of his own. Bosman's new home was discordant, in one of the poorer white suburbs, an overcrowded, bread-line community. Perhaps to escape this unleavened environment, he impulsively married, only to desert his bride to take up his first (and as it turns out last) posting in the Transvaal Education Department. He was sent to a one-roomed farm-school in the back of beyond, in a district called the Groot Marico, which most South Africans would never have heard of had he not chronicled it as he did, making it uniquely famous. The Groot Marico is the locus of almost all of his many short stories – as developed in loving detail as Hardy's Wessex, Leacock's Canadian small-town, or Steinbeck's Long Valley. He collected there sufficient raw material for over 160 pieces in only six months. As a young schoolmaster, with a certain status in this sprawling, underdeveloped rural never-never, he had fallen among informants who charged his writer's store with the very stuff of history, as yet unrecorded. His notebooks of the time show how he dutifully became the (English-language) scribe of an old-world, depressed, virtually pre-literate region which held the (Afrikaans-language) story of his and many other people.

Then, at mid-year, on holiday in Johannesburg, with a frontiersman's hunting rifle the Marico had taught him to use with accuracy, he committed the first of many acts which were to gain him a notorious kind of fame. In the stuffy colonial world of British Johannesburg, in the style of its gangland, he shot his step-brother dead in a late-night domestic quarrel. The trial was a sensation, aggravated by Bosman's refusal to defend himself; as he maintained his crime was motiveless, he accepted his fate without demur. He was sentenced to hang by the neck for it, in Pretoria Central Prison – the locus of a disproportionately large amount of South African literature that deals with political offences against the modern apartheid state. In 1926, however, it was a model British correctional institution, and in it Bosman was a common criminal. He was reprieved from the shadow of the gallows; his wife divorced him without his knowing; and at the end of the decade he was released on parole for good behaviour. It took him another nineteen years to come to terms with his jail experience; his novelized confession, *Cold Stone Jug* of 1949, is one of the many harrowing works in South African prison literature, and in some ways one of the most relentless.

Bosman faced the 1930s Depression as an ex-con and an outcast, with few resources. From prison he had smuggled out some fictional sketches which he discovered had been published pseudonymously. From then for the rest of his life he would live by his pen, either as a freelance writer or as a journalist. He worked on a succession of fly-by-night literary scandal-sheets which inventively became thorns in the rich flesh of the Johannesburg business scene; many landed him back in court again, or were banned. 'Makapan's Caves' and 'The Rooinek', the first two of his 'well-made' stories, seem to have come out during all this inglorious activity fully mature – with his Marico narrator,

Oom Schalk Lourens, he seems to have found overnight the mouthpiece that would keep him seriously at work for the next decade and more, virtually unchanged. The dryness, the canny insights, the withdrawn mockery of this stoep-talking patriarch are incredible coming from a man in his late twenties. But he was always more erudite and conscientious than he pretended, and he systematically set about distilling the shrewdness and the chaff of Mark Twain or Henry Lawson, the ironic structures of Bret Harte and O. Henry, the grotesque of Edgar Allan Poe and the impressionism of Stephen Crane and Lafcadio Hearn into this one figure – his Bushveld raconteur – drawn, too, from the concentration of life he had experienced in the Marico and in jail.

Although his South African readers today are fatally attracted to the story of Bosman's bizarre, cowboy life – and often quite unable to understand the immense scope of his literary sophistication – it must also be set down that the jail sentence destabilized him. What some call flair and even genius in the events of his later career was often only tawdry and mean. He was had up for organizing back-street abortions, extortion, blasphemy and petty crime, and the tenor of the rags he and his colleagues produced to catch pennies was often nauseatingly self-congratulatory. With complete cynicism he could turn the gutter-press's rackets into petty rip-offs, often masquerading his cronies' craven money-making schemes as acts of quixotic public benefaction. In 1934 when, with his second wife, he left in a hurry for London, he set up more of the same, running a crooked vanity press and working on a smear-sheet designed to push the Empire Movement – both were closed down. From this period, however, date some of the finest Oom Schalk stories, which are precisely about the British–South African bond in all its emotional complexity.

Repatriated to South Africa during the Second World War, Bosman seems to have wholly reformed. At least, he entered middle age more sedately; he edited a reputable newspaper in Pietersburg, Northern Transvaal (which gave him the material for his purple, Lawrentian first novel); his wife died tragically and he remarried; he settled finally in Johannesburg, working as a columnist and literary editor on various well-established magazines. From 1947 onwards he prolifically turned out interviews, art criticism, reviews, talk-of-the-town columns, and always short stories. His existence was as hand-to-mouth as ever, and by his fortieth birthday he was writing as if he knew he was on limited time. He had lived down his murderous past, too; when *Cold Stone Jug* appeared the respectable circles which he served could not credit that such a mordantly brutal past could connect with him. From these new, jovial, easy-going days dates the present, much-loved image of Bosman – his impish, debonair, slightly haunted face, wearing a Stetson at an angle.

With the advent of a weekly Johannesburg liberal paper, the *Forum*, in 1950 Bosman finished with Oom Schalk (whose range of experience covered 1870–1920), and updated the Marico tales to his present day. The second cycle of stories, which carries the overall title of 'In die Voorkamer', numbers some eighty in all, and was written for the *Forum* to a weekly deadline. This deadline correlates with the weekly arrival of the government postal lorry at Jurie Steyn's depot, and this format was Bosman's most golden opportunity to review the affairs of state through the prism of his backveld symposium. Hence the virtuoso 'conversation pieces' that are, really, fragments of a single, never-ending story, complete with a cast of recurring characters. The Marico, in these last stories, is more a locus in Bosman's fertile mind, more to do with the news-benches of Johannesburg than any actual geography, a place in which the news could be absorbed and personalized.

Under immense pressure, he also worked on plays, a final novel – his masterpiece, *Willemsdorp* – sub-editing, altering the first house he ever owned, writing literary essays, organizing his earlier work for publication, editing anthologies. The first collection of Oom Schalk stories, *Mafeking Road*, came out in a local publication in 1947 and immediately went into a flimsy and much reprinted paperback. He sickened and later died of a heart-attack in 1951 at the age of forty-six. A further twelve collections of his work have been published posthumously.

Bosman had made a difficult and exacting career decision early on – he decided to write, polemically and passionately, for a restricted audience, that of his contemporary South Africans. He was an Afrikaner, thoroughly Anglicized, in one of the world's intellectual backwaters, addressing his fellow colonials. While his contemporaries addressed themselves to metropolitan readerships – Eugène N. Marais, C. Louis Leipoldt, Alan Paton, and then Es'kia Mphahlele, Doris Lessing and Nadine Gordimer – as was the custom of the times, Bosman, perhaps because he knew where his best aesthetic interests lay, and with the dedication of a maniac, did everything in his power to reform the tastes of, and create a market among, an almost ignored readership, that of his own tight, humourless parish. While other colonial writers were contributing voluminously to English literature from abroad, like so many 'new literature' figures now come into prominence Bosman used English literature to enliven – indeed, in many ways to create – a doggedly indigenous literature. His literary patriotism was exemplary; throughout his career hardly a local periodical appeared without a new work of his. As a result, among the local circle he attained a reputation which none who experienced the living by-play of the way he exercised his art with an issue-by-issue relevance have forgotten. Devoted to that evanescent factor of topical relevance, he forfeited what many of his peers achieved, that magical status of 'international recognition'. Outside South Africa today his work is virtually unknown.

Many who knew the subtlety and the power of his work as it arose in the South African context have praised him and promoted him: Roy Campbell, William Plomer, David Wright; Doris Lessing, whose career began on one of the periodicals for which Bosman was literary editor, has called his *Cold Stone Jug* 'the saddest of all prison books', classing him along with Olive Schreiner and Eugène Marais as one of the few, rare talents bred out of the loneliness of the veld. When in 1963 his *Unto Dust* collection appeared in the United Kingdom, *The Times Literary Supplement* curtly dismissed it as misapplied nostalgia for an age which, one has to agree, from the perspective of post-Sharpeville South Africa might appear to be irrelevant. But Bosman died only three years into apartheid times; even then, he was not slow to respond to early segregatory legislation – in 'White Ant' he witheringly pillories the issue of the separation of voters' rolls, in 'Unto Dust' he gives the social segregations of petty apartheid, which in South Africa persist even beyond the grave, a feverish, nightmare cast, and no writer has dealt more poignantly – or more confrontationally – with the race reclassification laws than Bosman has in 'Birth Certificate'. Bosman's record on human rights issues is immaculate.

Bosman did belong to a prior, less publicly racist era. But the difficult part of Bosman to absorb, and the quality which places him centrally in the South African canon, is that his analyses of the pre-apartheid British world are never idealized or sentimentalized. On the contrary, Bosman never lets the guilty race memory off the hook. His main theme is always how the roots of the present lie in the past. He always allegorizes the nineteenth century into the first half of the twentieth; thus, transpose Bosman's work from the first half of the twentieth century into the present, and his message is devastatingly clear – apartheid was not born overnight. No one who sees what Bosman is talking about can feel quite the same about the South African situation again. Behind the uneasy humour, the wry throw-away, lie substructures deeper than many other writers have perceived. And in contemporary South Africa, where the system survives on the extinction of memory, Bosman is almost the only writer who kept such useful records. The more the memory fails us, the greater his stature becomes.

This selection includes twenty-seven of his stories, covering from first to last of his working life. Eight of these stories appear in a collection for the first time. The arrangement is approximately chronological, both in terms of the order of composition and in terms of the historical events against which the stories resonate. No matter how one arranges Bosman's stories, a hidden agenda seems always to emerge – he always situated his characters in relation to larger events, and here we have the whole range, from the *Flying Dutchman*'s cursed landfall at the Cape of Good Hope onwards to the 1950s. Juxtaposed as they are, they tell a tale which is larger than the sum of its pieces. The precision of each implies an immensely articulated panorama, sometimes too humanly rich and too wretched to contemplate. Here is a cross-section of that larger tale, for the record.

Stephen Gray
Johannesburg, 1986

Makapan's Caves

Kaffirs? (said Oom Schalk Lourens). Yes, I know them. And they're all the same. I fear the Almighty, and I respect His works, but I could never understand why He made the kaffir and the rinderpest. The Hottentot is a little better. The Hottentot will only steal the biltong hanging out on the line to dry. He won't steal the line as well. That is where the kaffir is different.

Still, sometimes you come across a good kaffir, who is faithful and upright and a true Christian and doesn't let the wild-dogs catch the sheep. I always think that it isn't right to kill that kind of kaffir.

I remember about one kaffir we had, by the name of Nongaas. How we got him was after this fashion. It was in the year of the big drought, when there was no grass, and the water in the pan had dried up. Our cattle died like flies. It was terrible. Every day ten or twelve or twenty died. So my father said we must pack everything on the waggons and trek up to the Dwarsberge, where he heard there had been good rains. I was six years old, then, the youngest in the family. Most of the time I sat in the back of the waggon, with my mother and my two sisters. My brother Hendrik was seventeen, and he helped my father and the kaffirs to drive on our cattle. That was how we trekked. Many more of our cattle died along the way, but after about two months we got into the Lowveld and my father said that God had been good to us. For the grass was green along the Dwarsberge.

One morning we came to some kaffir huts, where my father bartered two sacks of mealies for a roll of tobacco. A piccanin of about my own age was standing in front of a hut, and he looked at us all the time and grinned. But mostly he looked at my brother Hendrik. And that was not a wonder, either. Even in those days my brother Hendrik was careful about his appearance, and he always tried to be fashionably dressed. On Sundays he even wore socks. When we had loaded up the mealies, my father cut off a plug of Boer tobacco and gave it to the piccanin, who grinned still more, so that we saw every one of his teeth, which were very white. He put the plug in his mouth and bit it. Then we all laughed. The piccanin looked just like a puppy that has swallowed a piece of meat, and turns his head sideways, to see how it tastes.

That was in the morning. We went right on until the afternoon, for my father wanted to reach Tweekoppiesfontein, where we were going to stand with our cattle for some time. It was late in the afternoon when we got there, and we started to outspan. Just as I was getting off the waggon, I looked round and saw something jumping quickly behind a bush. It looked like some animal, so I was afraid, and told my brother Hendrik, who took up his gun and walked slowly towards the bush. We saw, directly afterwards, that it was the piccanin whom we had seen that morning in front of the hut. He must have been following behind our waggons for about ten miles. He looked dirty and tired, but when my brother went up to him he began to grin again, and seemed very happy. We didn't know what to do with him, so Hendrik shouted to him to go home, and started throwing stones at him. But my father was a merciful man, and after he had heard Nongaas story – for that was the name of the piccanin – he said he could stay with us, but he must be good, and not tell lies and steal, like the other kaffirs. Nongaas told us in the Sechuana language, which my father understood, that his father and mother had been killed by the lions, and that he was living with his uncle, whom he didn't like, but that he liked my brother Hendrik, and that was why he had followed our waggons.

Nongaas remained with us for many years. He grew up with us. He was a very good kaffir, and as time went by he became much attached to all of us. But he worshipped my brother Hendrik. As he grew older, my father sometimes spoke to Nongaas about his soul, and explained to him about God. But although he told my father that he understood, I could see that whenever Nongaas thought of God, he was really only thinking of Hendrik.

It was just after my twenty-first birthday that we got news that Hermanus Potgieter and his whole family had been killed by a kaffir tribe under Makapan. They also said that, after killing him, the kaffirs stripped off old Potgieter's skin and made wallets out of it in which to carry their dagga. It was very wicked of the kaffirs to have done that, especially as dagga makes you mad and it is a sin to smoke it. A commando was called up from our district to go and attack the tribe and teach them to have respect for the white man's laws – and above all, to have more respect for the white man's skin. My mother and sisters baked a great deal of harde beskuit, which we packed up, together with mealie-meal and biltong. We also took out the lead mould and melted bullets. The next morning my brother and I set out on horseback for Makapan's kraal. We were accompanied by Nongaas, whom we took along with us to look after the horses and light the fires. My father stayed at home. He said that he was too old to go on commando, unless it was to fight the red-coats, if there were still any left.

But he gave us some good advice.

'Don't forget to read your Bible, my sons,' he called out as we rode away. 'Pray the Lord to help you, and when you shoot always aim for the stomach.' These remarks were typical of my father's deeply religious nature, and he also knew that it was easier to hit a man in the stomach than in the head: and it is just as good, because no man can live long after his intestines have been shot away.

Well, we rode on, my brother and I with Nongaas following a few yards behind us on the pack-horse. Now and again we fell in with other burghers, many of whom brought their waggons with them, until, on the third day, we reached Makapan's kraal, where the big commando had already gone into camp. We got there in the evening, and everywhere as far as we could see there were fires burning in a big circle. There were over two hundred waggons, and on their tents the fires shone red and yellow. We reported ourselves to the veld-kornet, who showed us a place where we could camp, next to the four Van Rensburg brothers. Nongaas had just made the fire and boiled the coffee when one of the Van

Rensburgs came up and invited us over to their waggon. They had shot a rietbok and were roasting pieces of it on the coals.

We all shook hands and said it was good weather for the mealies if only the ruspes didn't eat them, and that it was time we had another president, and that rietbok tasted very fine when roasted on the coals. Then they told us what had happened about the kaffirs. Makapan and his followers had seen the commandos coming from a distance, and after firing a few shots at them had all fled into the caves in the krantz. These caves stretched away underground very far and with many turnings. So, as the Boers could not storm the kaffirs without losing heavily, the commandant gave instructions that the ridge was to be surrounded and the kaffirs starved out. They were all inside the caves, the whole tribe, men, women and children. They had already been there six days, and as they couldn't have much food left, and as there was only a small dam with brackish water, we were hopeful of being able to kill off most of the kaffirs without wasting ammunition.

Already, when the wind blew towards us from the mouth of the caves, the stink was terrible. We would have pitched our camp further back, only that we were afraid some of the kaffirs would escape between the fires.

The following morning I saw for the first time why we couldn't drive the kaffirs from their lairs, even though our commando was four hundred strong. All over, through the rocks and bushes, I could see black openings in the krantz, that led right into the deep parts of the earth. Here and there we could see dead bodies lying. But there were still left a lot of kaffirs that were not dead, and them we could not see. But they had guns, which they had bought from the illicit traders and the missionaries, and they shot at us whenever we came within range. And all the time there was that stench of decaying bodies.

For another week the siege went on. Then we heard that our leaders, Marthinus Wessels Pretorius and Paul Kruger, had quarrelled. Kruger wanted to attack the kaffirs immediately and finish the affair, but Pretorius said it was too dangerous and he didn't want any more burghers killed. He said that already the hand of the Lord lay heavy upon Makapan, and in another few weeks, the kaffirs would all be dead of starvation. But Paul Kruger said that it would even be better if the hand of the Lord lay still heavier upon the kaffirs. Eventually Paul Kruger obtained permission to take fifty volunteers and storm the caves from one side, while Commandant Piet Potgieter was to advance from the other side with two hundred men, to distract the attention of the kaffirs. Kruger was popular with all of us and nearly everyone volunteered to go with him. So he picked fifty men, among whom were the Van Rensburgs and my brother. Therefore, as I did not want to stay behind and guard the camp, I had to join Piet Potgieter's commando.

All the preparations were made, and the following morning we got ready to attack. My brother Hendrik was very proud and happy at having been chosen for the more dangerous part. He oiled his gun very carefully and polished up his veldskoens.

Then Nongaas came up and I noticed that he looked very miserable.

'My baas,' he said to my brother Hendrik, 'you mustn't go and fight. They'll shoot you dead.'

My brother shook his head.

'Then let me go with you, baas,' Nongaas said, 'I will go in front and look after you.'

Hendrik only laughed.

'Look here, Nongaas,' he said, 'you can stay behind and cook the dinner. I will get back in time to eat it.'

The whole commando came together and we all knelt down and prayed. Then Marthinus Wessels Pretorius said we must sing Hymn Number 23, 'Rest my soul, thy God is king'. Furthermore, we sang another hymn and also a psalm. Most people would have thought that one hymn would be enough. But not so Pretorius. He always made quite sure of everything he did. Then we moved off to the attack. We fought bravely, but the kaffirs were many, and they lay in the darkness of the caves, and shot at us without our being able to see them. While the fighting lasted it was worse than the lyddite bombs at Paardeberg. And the stench was terrible. We tied handkerchiefs round the lower part of our face, but that did not help. Also, since we were not Englishmen, many of us had no handkerchiefs. Still we fought on, shooting at an enemy we could not see. We rushed right up to the mouth of one of the caves, and even got some distance into it, when our leader, Commandant Piet Potgieter, flung up his hands and fell backwards, shot through the breast. We carried him out, but he was quite dead. So we lost heart and retired.

When we returned from the fight we found that the other attacking party had also been defeated. They had shot many kaffirs, but there were still hundreds of them left, who fought all the more fiercely with hunger gnawing at their bellies.

I went back to our camp. There was only Nongaas, sitting forward on a stone, with his face on his arms. An awful fear clutched me as I asked him what was wrong.

'Baas Hendrik,' he replied, and as he looked at me in his eyes there was much sorrow, 'Baas Hendrik did not come back.'

I went out immediately and made inquiries, but nobody could tell me anything for sure. They remembered quite well seeing my brother Hendrik when they stormed the cave. He was right in among the foremost of the attackers. When I heard that, I felt a great pride in my brother, although I also knew that nothing else could be expected of the son of my father. But no man could tell me what had happened to him. All they knew was that when they got back he was not among them.

I spoke to Marthinus Wessels Pretorius and asked him to send out another party to seek for my brother. But Pretorius was angry.

'I will not allow one more man,' he replied. 'It was all Kruger's doing. I was against it from the start. Now Commandant Potgieter has been killed, who was a better man than Kruger and all his Dopper clique put together. If any man goes back to the caves I shall discharge him from the commando.'

But I don't think it was right of Pretorius. Because Paul Kruger was only trying to do his duty, and afterwards, when he was nominated for president, I voted for him.

It was eleven o'clock when I again reached our part of the laager. Nongaas was still sitting on the flat stone, and I saw that he had carried out my brother Hendrik's instructions, and that the pot was boiling on the fire. The dinner was ready, but my brother was not there. That sight was too much for me, and I went and lay down alone under the Van Rensburgs' waggon.

I looked up again, about half an hour later, and I saw Nongaas walking away with a water-bottle and a small sack strapped to his back. He said nothing to me, but I knew he was going to look for my brother Hendrik. Nongaas knew that if his baas was still alive he would need him. So he went to him. That was all. For a long while I watched Nongaas as he crept along through the rocks and bushes. I supposed it was his intention to lie in wait near one of the caves and then crawl inside when the night came. That was a very brave thing to do. If Makapan's kaffirs saw him they would be sure to kill him, because he was helping the Boers against them, and also because he was a Bechuana.

The evening came, but neither my brother Hendrik nor Nongaas. All that night I sat with my face to the caves and never slept. Then in the morning I got up and loaded my gun. I said to myself that if Nongaas had been killed in the attempt there was only one thing left for me to do. I myself must go to my brother.

I walked out first into the veld, in case one of the officers saw me and made me come back. Then I walked along the ridge and got under cover, hiding in the long grass and behind the stones, so that I came to one part of Makapan's stronghold where things were more quiet. I got to within about two hundred yards of a cave. There I lay very still, behind a big rock, to find out if there were any kaffirs watching from that side. Occasionally I heard the sound of a shot being fired, but that was far away. Afterwards I fell asleep, for I was very weary with the anxiety and through not having slept the night before.

When I woke up the sun was right overhead. It was hot and there were no clouds in the sky. Only there were a few aasvoëls, which flew round and round very slowly, without ever seeming to flap their wings. Now and again one of them would fly down and settle on the ground, and it was very horrible. I thought of my brother Hendrik and shivered. I looked towards the cave. Inside it seemed as though there was something moving. A minute later I saw that it was a kaffir coming stealthily towards the entrance.

He appeared to be looking in my direction, and for fear that he should see me and call the other kaffirs, I jumped up quickly and shot at him, aiming at the stomach. He fell over like a sack of potatoes and I was thankful for my father's advice. But I had to act quickly. If the other kaffirs had heard the shot they would all come running up at once. And I didn't want that to happen. I didn't like the look of those aasvoëls. So I decided to take a great risk. Accordingly I ran as fast as I could towards the cave and rushed right into it, so that, even if the kaffirs did come, they wouldn't see me amongst the shadows. For a long time I lay down and waited. But as no more kaffirs came, I got up and walked slowly down a dark passage, looking round every time to see that nobody followed me, and to make sure that I would find my way back. For there were many twists and turnings, and the whole krantz seemed to be hollowed out.

I knew that my search would be very difficult. But there was something that seemed to tell me that my brother was near by. So I was strong in my faith, and I knew that the Lord would lead me aright. And I found my brother Hendrik, and he was alive. It was with a feeling of great joy that I came across him. I saw him in the dim light that came through a big split in the roof. He was lying against a boulder, holding his leg and groaning. I saw afterwards that his leg was sprained and much swollen, but that was all that was wrong. So great was my brother Hendrik's surprise at seeing me that at first he could not talk. He just held my hand and laughed softly, and when I touched his forehead I knew that he was feverish. I gave him some brandy out of my flask, and in a few words he told me all that had happened. When they stormed the cave he was right in front and as the kaffirs retreated he followed them up. But they all ran in different ways, until my brother found himself alone. He tried to get back, but lost his way and fell down a dip. In that way he sprained his ankle so severely that he had been in agony all the time. He crawled into a far corner and remained there, with the danger and the darkness and his pain. But the worst of all was the stink of the rotting bodies.

'Then Nongaas came,' my brother Hendrik said.

'Nongaas?' I asked him.

'Yes,' he replied. 'He found me and gave me food and water, and carried me on his back. Then the water gave out and I was very thirsty. So Nongaas took the bottle to go and fill it at the pan. But it is very dangerous to get there, and I am so frightened they may kill him.'

'They will not kill him,' I said. 'Nongaas will come back.' I said that, but in my heart I was afraid. For the caves were many and dark, and the kaffirs were blood-mad. It would not do to wait. So I lifted Hendrik on my shoulder and carried him towards the entrance. He was in much pain.

'You know,' he whispered, 'Nongaas was crying when he found me. He thought I was dead. He has been very good to me – so very good. Do you remember that day when he followed behind our waggons? He looked so very trustful and so little, and yet I – I threw stones at him. I wish I did not do that. I only hope that he comes back safe. He was crying and stroking my hair.'

As I said, my brother Hendrik was feverish.

'Of course he will come back,' I answered him. But this time I knew that I lied. For as I came through the mouth of the cave I kicked against the kaffir I had shot there. The body sagged over to one side and I saw the face.

Yellow Moepels

If ever you spoke to my father about witchdoctors (Oom Schalk Lourens said), he would always relate one story. And at the end of it he would explain that, while a witchdoctor could foretell the future for you from the bones, at the same time he could only tell you the things that didn't matter. My father used to say that the important things were as much hidden from the witchdoctor as from the man who listened to his prophecy.

My father said that when he was sixteen he went with his friend, Paul, a stripling of about his own age, to a kaffir witch-doctor. They had heard that this witchdoctor was very good at throwing the bones. My father said they only went on that one occasion out of boyish curiosity. But they never went again.

This witchdoctor lived alone in a mud hut. While they were still on the way to the hut the two youths laughed and jested, but as soon as they got inside they felt different. They were impressed. The witchdoctor was very old and very wrinkled. He had on a queer headdress made up from the tails of different wild animals. But for the rest he was clad, simply but neatly, in a woman's pink petticoat. My father says that those were very uncivilized times.

You could tell that the boys were overawed as they sat there on the floor in the dark. Because my father, who had meant to hand the witchdoctor only a plug of Boer tobacco, gave him a whole roll. And Paul, who had said, when they were outside, that he was going to give him nothing at all, actually handed over his hunting knife.

And all that happened while the witchdoctor was just looking at the boys, without talking. My father said afterwards that he was glad the witchdoctor didn't go on looking at him like that much longer. For then he would have given him his veldskoens, also. And it would have been no joke walking back barefoot through the thorns.

Yes, you could see that he was a good witchdoctor.

Then he threw the bones. He threw them first for my father. He told him many things. He told him that he would grow up to be a good burgher, and that he would one day be very prosperous. He would have a big farm and many cattle and two ox-waggons.

But what the witchdoctor did not tell my father was that in years to come he would have a son, Schalk, who could tell better stories than any man in the Marico. I suppose the witchdoctor was afraid to tell him that, in case my father took back the roll of Boer tobacco.

Then the witchdoctor threw the bones for Paul. For a long while he was silent. He looked from the bones to Paul, and back to the bones, in a strange way. Then he spoke.

'I can see you go far away, my kleinbaas,' he said, 'very far away over the great waters. Away from your own land, my kleinbaas.'

'And the veld?' Paul asked, 'and the krantzes and the vlaktes?'

'And away from your own people,' the witchdoctor said.

'And will I – will I –'

'No, my kleinbasie,' the witchdoctor answered, 'you will not come back. You will die there.'

My father said that when they came out of that hut Paul Kruger's face was very white. That was why my father used to say that, while a witchdoctor could tell you true things, he could not tell you the things that really mattered.

And my father was right.

Take the case of Neels Potgieter and Martha Rossouw, for instance. They became engaged to be married just before the affair at Paardekraal. There, on the hoogte, our leaders pointed out to us that, although the Transvaal had been annexed by Sir Theophilus Shepstone, it nevertheless meant that we would have to go on paying taxes just the same. Everybody knew then that it was war.

Neels Potgieter and I were in the same commando.

It was arranged that the burghers of the neighbourhood should assemble at the veld-kornet's house. Instructions had also been given that no women were to be present. There was much fighting to be done, and this final leave-taking was likely to be an embarrassing thing.

Nevertheless, as always, the women came. And among them was Neels's sweetheart, Martha Rossouw. And also there was my sister, Annie.

I shall never forget that scene in front of the veld-kornet's house, in the early morning, when there were still shadows on the rante, and a thin wind blew through the grass. We had no predikant there; but an ouderling, with two bandoliers slung across his body, and a Martini in his hand, said a few words. He was a strong and simple man, with no great gifts of oratory. But when he spoke about the Transvaal we could feel what was in his heart, and we took off our hats in silence.

And it was not very long afterwards that I again took off my hat in much the same way. Then it was at Majuba Hill. It was after the battle, and the ouderling still had his two bandoliers around him when we buried him at the foot of the koppie.

But what impressed me most was the prayer that followed the ouderling's brief address. In front of the veld-kornet's house we knelt, each burgher with his rifle at his side. And the women-folk knelt down with us. And the wind seemed very gentle as it stirred the tall grass-blades; very gentle as it swept over the bared heads of the men and fluttered the kappies and skirts of the women; very gentle as it carried the prayers of our nation over the veld.

After that we stood up and sang a hymn. The ceremony was over. The agterryers brought us our horses. And, dry-eyed and tight-lipped, each woman sent her man forth to war. There was no weeping.

Then, in accordance with Boer custom, we fired a volley into the air.

'Voorwaarts, burghers,' came the veld-kornet's order, and we cantered down the road in twos. But before we left I had overheard Neels Potgieter say something to Martha Rossouw as he leant out of the saddle and kissed her. My sister Annie, standing beside my horse, also heard.

'When the moepels are ripe, Martha,' Neels said, 'I will come to you again.'

Annie and I looked at each other and smiled. It was a pretty thing that Neels had said. But then Martha was also pretty. More pretty than the veld-trees that bore those yellow moepels, I reflected – and more wild.

I was still thinking of this when our commando had passed over the bult, in a long line, on our way to the south, where Natal was, and the other commandos, and Majuba.

This was the war of Bronkhorst Spruit and General Colley and Laing's Nek. You have no doubt heard many accounts of this war, some of them truthful, perhaps. For it is a singular thing that, as a man grows older, and looks back on fights that he has been in, he keeps on remembering, each year, more and more of the enemy that he has shot. Each year, also, he remembers more and more brave deeds that he has done.

It is strange that war should make a man forget, at the time, what exactly he did for his country, and only allow him to remember, twenty years later, that it was he alone that did nearly all the fighting.

Klaas Uys was a man like that. Each year, on his birthday, he remembered one or two more red-coats that he had shot, whereupon he got up straight away and put another few notches in the wood part of his rifle, along the barrel. Another man might have waited until next day. But not so Klaas. He cut those extra notches the moment he remembered about them, so that nobody could come along and dispute his total afterwards. Klaas was great on accuracy.

Originally he had started near the muzzle with those notches, but when I last saw him he had got well down towards the lower end of the rifle, where it presses against your shoulder. And he said his memory was getting better every year.

Once, in my presence, Klaas Uys told an Englishman about the fighting he had done.

'Do you remember the Battle of — ?' the Englishman asked him, afterwards, mentioning a foreign place that I had never heard of before – and that I am sure Klaas hadn't heard of, either. But you couldn't trap Klaas Uys as easily as all that.

'Oh, yes,' he answered, 'I fought right through it. I shot seventeen red-coats in the tamboekie grass.'

'And Wellington?' the Englishman asked, 'did you see him?'

'I fired at him twice,' Klaas Uys admitted, 'but I missed him. He ran away so fast through the mealielands.'

The Englishman did not answer. He looked very far out across the veld. I suppose he was thinking about how fine it must be to belong to a nation that could produce as fearless a fighting man as Klaas Uys.

All the time I was on commando, I received only one letter. That came from Annie, my sister. She said I was not to take any risks, and that I must keep far away from the English, especially if they had guns. She also said I was to remember that I was a white man, and that if there was any dangerous work to be done, I had to send a kaffir out to do it.

There were more things like that in Annie's letter. But I had no need of her advice. Our commandant was a God-fearing and wily man, and he knew even better ways than Annie did for keeping out of range of the enemy's fire.

But Annie also said, at the end of her letter, that she and Martha Rossouw had gone to a witchdoctor. They had gone to find out about Neels Potgieter and me. Now, if I had been at home, I would not have permitted Annie to indulge in this nonsense.

Especially as the witchdoctor said to her, 'Yes, missus, I can see Baas Schalk Lourens. He will come back safe. He is very clever, Baas Schalk. He lies behind a big stone, with a dirty brown blanket pulled over his head. And he stays behind that stone until the fighting is finished – quite finished.'

According to Annie's letter, the witchdoctor told her a few other things about me, too. But I won't bother to repeat them now. I think I have said enough to show you what sort of a scoundrel that old kaffir was. He not only took advantage of the credulity of a simple girl, but he also tried to be funny at the expense of a young man who was fighting for his country's freedom.

What was more, Annie said that she recognized it was me right away, just from the kaffir's description of that blanket.

To Martha Rossouw the witchdoctor said, 'Baas Neels Potgieter will come back to you, missus, when the moepels are ripe again. At sun-under he will come.'

That was all he said about Neels, and there wasn't very much in that, anyway, seeing that Neels himself – except for the bit about the sunset – had made the very same prophecy the day the commando set out. I suppose that witchdoctor had been too busy thinking out foolish and spiteful things about me to be able to give any attention to Neels Potgieter's affairs.

But I didn't mention Annie's letter to Neels. He might have wanted to know more than I was willing to tell him. More, even, perhaps, than Martha was willing to tell him – Martha of the wild heart.

Then, at last, the war ended, and over the Transvaal the vierkleur waved again. And the commandos went home by their different ways. And our leaders revived their old quarrels as to who should be president. And, everywhere, except for a number of lonely graves on hillside and in vlakte, things were as they had been before Shepstone came.

It was getting on towards evening when our small band rode over the bult again, and once more came to a halt at the veld-kornet's house. A messenger had been sent on in advance to announce our coming, and from far around the women and children and old men had gathered to welcome their victorious burghers back from the war. And there were tears in many eyes when we sang, 'Hef, burghers, hef.'

And the moepels were ripe and yellow on the trees.

And in the dusk Neels Potgieter found Martha Rossouw and kissed her. At sundown, as the witchdoctor had said. But there was one important thing that the witchdoctor had not told. It was something that Neels Potgieter did not know, either, just then. And that was that Martha did not want him any more.

The Red Coat

I have spoken before of some of the queer things that happen to your mind through fever (Oom Schalk Lourens said). In the past there was a good deal more fever in the Marico and Waterberg districts than there is today. And you got it in a much more severe form, too. Today you still get malaria in these parts, of course. But your temperature doesn't go so high any more before the fever breaks. And you are not left as weak after an attack of malaria as you were in the old days. Nor do you often get illusions of the sort that afterwards came to trouble the mind of Andries Visagie.

They say that this improvement is due to civilization.

Well, I suppose that must be right. For one thing, we now have a government lorry from Zeerust every week with letters and newspapers and catalogues from Johannesburg shopkeepers. And only three years ago Jurie Bekker bought a wooden stand with a glass that a trader brought to him for measuring how much rain Jurie Bekker gets on his farm. Jurie Bekker is very proud of his rain-gauge, too, and will accompany any white visitor to the back of his house to show him how well it works. 'We have had no rain for the last three years,' Jurie Bekker will explain, 'and that is exactly what the rain-gauge records, also. Look, you can see for yourself. Nil.'

Jurie Bekker also tried to explain the rain instrument to the kaffirs on his farm. But he gave it up. 'A kaffir with a blanket on hasn't got the brain to understand a white man's inventions,' Jurie Bekker said about it, afterwards. 'When I showed my kaffirs what this rain-gauge was all about, they just stood in a long row and laughed.'

Nevertheless, I must admit that, with this civilization we are getting here, the malaria fever has not of recent years been the scourge it was in the old days.

The story of Andries Visagie and his fever begins at the Battle of Bronkhorst Spruit. It was at the Battle of Bronkhorst Spruit that Andries Visagie had his life saved by Piet Niemand, according to all accounts. And yet it was also arising out of that incident that many people in this part of the Marico in later years came to the conclusion that Andries Visagie was somebody whose word you could not take seriously, because of the suffering that he had undergone.

You know, of course, that the Bronkhorst Spruit battle was fought very long ago. In those days we still called the English red-coats. For the English soldiers wore red jackets that we could see against the khaki colour of the tamboekie grass for almost as far as the bullets from our Martini-Henry rifles could carry. That shows you how uncivilized those times were.

I often heard Piet Niemand relate the story of how he found Andries Visagie lying unconscious in a donga on the battlefield, and of how he revived him with brandy that he had in his water-bottle.

Piet Niemand explained that, from the number of red-coats that were lined up at Bronkhorst Spruit that morning, he could see it was going to be a serious engagement, and so he had thoughtfully emptied all the water out of his bottle and had replaced it with Magaliesberg peach brandy of the rawest kind he could get. Piet Niemand said that he was advancing against the English when he came across that donga. He was advancing very fast and was looking neither to right nor left of him, he said. And he would draw lines on any piece of paper that was handy to show you the direction he took.

I can still remember how annoyed we all were when a young school-teacher, looking intently at that piece of paper, said that if that was the direction in which Piet Niemand was advancing, then it must have meant that the English had got right to behind the Boer lines, which was contrary to what he had read in the history books. Shortly afterwards Hannes Potgieter, who was chairman of our school committee, got that young school-teacher transferred.

As Hannes Potgieter said, that young school-teacher with his history-book ideas had never been in a battle and didn't know what real fighting was. In the confusion of a fight, with guns going off all round you, Hannes Potgieter declared, it was not unusual for a burgher to find himself advancing away from the enemy – and quite fast, too.

He was not ashamed to admit that a very similar thing had happened to him at one stage of the Battle of Majuba Hill. He had run back a long way, because he had suddenly felt that he wanted to make sure that the kaffir agterryers were taking proper care of the horses. But he need have had no fears on that score, Hannes Potgieter added. Because when he reached the sheltered spot among the thorn-trees where the horses were tethered, he found that three commandants and a veld-kornet had arrived there before him, on the same errand. The veld-kornet was so anxious to reassure himself that the horses were all right, that he was even trying to mount one of them.

When Hannes Potgieter said that, he winked. And we all laughed. For we knew that he had fought bravely at Majuba Hill. But he was also ready always to acknowledge that he had been very frightened at Majuba Hill. And because he had been in several wars, he did not like to hear the courage of Piet Niemand called in question. What Hannes Potgieter meant us to understand was that if, at the Battle of Bronkhorst Spruit, Piet Niemand did perhaps run at one stage, it was the sort of thing that could happen to any man; and for which any man could be forgiven, too.

And, in any case, Piet Niemand's story was interesting enough. He said that in the course of his advance he came across a donga, on the edge of which a thorn-bush was growing. The donga was about ten foot deep. He descended into the donga to light his pipe. He couldn't light his pipe out there on the open veld, because it was too windy, he said. When he reached the bottom of the donga, he also found that he had brought most of that thorn-bush along with him.

Then, in a bend of the donga, Piet Niemand saw what he thought was an English soldier, lying face downwards. He thought, at first, that the English soldier had come down there to light his pipe, also, and had decided to stay longer. He couldn't see too clearly, Piet Niemand said, because the smoke of the Battle of Bronkhorst Spruit had got into his eyes. Maybe the smoke from his pipe, too, I thought. That is, if what he was lighting up there in the donga was Piet Retief roll tobacco.

Why Piet Niemand thought that the man lying at the bend of the donga was an Englishman was because he was wearing a red coat. But in the next moment Piet Niemand realized that the man was not an Englishman. For the man's neck was not also red.

Immediately there flashed into Piet Niemand's mind the suspicion that the man was a Boer in English uniform – a Transvaal Boer fighting against his own people. If it had been an Englishman lying there, he would have called on him to surrender, Piet Niemand said, but a Boer traitor he was going to shoot without giving him a chance to get up.

He was in the act of raising his Martini-Henry to fire, when the truth came to him. And that was how he first met Andries Visagie and how he came to save his life. He saw that while Andries Visagie's coat was indeed red, it was not with dye, but with the blood from his wound. Piet Niemand said that he was so overcome at the thought of the sin he had been about to commit that when he unstrapped his water-bottle his knees trembled as much as did his fingers. But when Piet Niemand told this part of his story, Hannes Potgieter said that he need not make any excuses for himself, especially as no harm had come of it. If it had been a Boer traitor instead of Piet Niemand who had found himself in that same situation, Hannes Potgieter said, then the Boer traitor would have fired in any case, without bothering very much as to whether it was a Boer or an Englishman that he was shooting.

Piet Niemand knelt down beside Andries Visagie and turned him round and succeeded in pouring a quantity of brandy down his throat. Andries Visagie was not seriously wounded, but he had a high fever, from the sun and through loss of blood, and he spoke strange words.

That was the story that Piet Niemand had to tell.

Afterwards Andries Visagie made a good recovery in the mill at Bronkhorst Spruit that the commandant had turned into a hospital. And they say it was very touching to observe Andries Visagie's gratitude when Piet Niemand came to visit him.

Andries Visagie lay on the floor, on a rough mattress filled with grass and dried mealie-leaves. Piet Niemand went and sat on the floor beside him. They conversed. By that time Andries Visagie had recovered sufficiently to remember that he had shot three red-coats for sure. He added, however, that as the result of the weakness caused by his wound, his mind was not always very clear, at times. But when he got quite well and strong again, he would remember better. And then he would not be at all surprised if he remembered that he had also shot a general, he said.

Piet Niemand then related some of his own acts of bravery. And because they were both young men it gave them much pleasure to pass themselves off as heroes in each other's company.

Piet Niemand had already stood up to go when Andries Visagie reached his hand underneath the mattress and pulled out a watch with a heavy gold chain. The watch was shaped like an egg and on the case were pictures of angels, painted in enamel. Even without those angels, it would have been a very magnificent watch. But with those angels painted on the case, you would not care much if the watch did not go, even, and you still had to tell the time from the sun, holding your hand cupped over your eyes.

'I inherited this watch from my grandfather,' Andries Visagie said. 'He brought it with him on the Great Trek. You saved my life in the donga. You must take this watch as a keepsake.'

Those who were present at this incident in the temporary hospital at Bronkhorst Spruit said that Piet Niemand reached over to receive the gift. He almost had his hand on the watch, they say. And then he changed his mind and stood up straight.

'What I did was nothing,' Piet Niemand said. 'It was something anybody would have done. Anybody that was brave enough, I mean. But I want no reward for it. Maybe I'll some day buy myself a watch like that.'

Andries Visagie kept his father's father's egg-shaped watch, after all. But in his having offered Piet Niemand his most treasured possession, and in Piet Niemand having declined to accept it, there was set the seal on the friendship of those two young men. This friendship was guarded, maybe, by the wings of the angels painted in enamel on the watch-case. Afterwards people were to say that it was a pity Andries Visagie should have turned so queer in the head. It must have been that he had suffered too much, these people said.

In gratitude for their services in the First Boer War, the government of the Transvaal Republic made grants of farming land in the Waterberg district to those Boers on commando who had no ground of their own. The government of the Transvaal Republic did not think it necessary to explain that the area in question was already occupied – by lions and malaria mosquitoes and hostile kaffirs. Nevertheless, many Boers knew the facts about that part of the Waterberg pretty well. So only a handful of burghers were prepared to accept government farms. Most of the others felt that, seeing they had just come out of one war, there was not much point in going straight back to another.

All the same, a number of burghers did go and take up land in that area, and to everybody's surprise – not least to the surprise of the government, I suppose – they fared reasonably well. And among those new settlers in the Waterberg were Piet Niemand and Andries Visagie. Their farms were not more than two days' journey apart. So you could almost say they were neighbours. They visited each other regularly.

The years went by, and then in a certain wet season Andries Visagie lay stricken with malaria. And in his delirium he said strange things. Fancying himself back again at Bronkhorst Spruit, Andries Visagie said he could remember the long line of English generals he was shooting. He was shooting them full of medals, he said.

But there was another thing that Andries Visagie said he remembered then. And after he recovered from the malaria he still insisted that the circumstance he had recalled during his illness was the truth. He said that through that second bout of fever he was able to remember what had happened years before, in the donga, when he was also delirious.

And it was then that many of the farmers in the Waterberg began to say what a pity it was that Andries Visagie's illness should so far have affected his mind. For Andries Visagie said that he could remember distinctly, now, that time when he was lying in the donga. And he would never, of course, know who shot him. But what he did remember was that when Piet Niemand was bending over him, holding a water-bottle in his hand, Piet Niemand was wearing a red coat.

Unto Dust

I have noticed that when a young man or woman dies, people get the feeling that there is something beautiful and touching in the event, and that it is different from the death of an old person. In the thought, say, of a girl of twenty sinking into an untimely grave, there is a sweet wistfulness that makes people talk all kinds of romantic words. She died, they say, young, she that was so full of life and so fair. She was a flower that withered before it bloomed, they say, and it all seems so fitting and beautiful that there is a good deal of resentment, at the funeral, over the crude questions that a couple of men in plain clothes from the land-drost's office are asking about cattle-dip.

But when you have grown old, nobody is very much interested in the manner of your dying. Nobody except you yourself, that is. And I think that your past life has got a lot to do with the way you feel when you get near the end of your days. I remember how, when he was lying on his death-bed, Andries Wessels kept on telling us that it was because of the blameless path he had trodden from his earliest years that he could compose himself in peace to lay down his burdens. And I certainly never saw a man breathe his last more tranquilly, seeing that right up to the end he kept on murmuring to us how happy he was, with heavenly hosts and invisible choirs of angels all around him.

Just before he died, he told us that the angels had even become visible. They were medium-sized angels, he said, and they had cloven hoofs and carried forks. It was obvious that Andries Wessels' ideas were getting a bit confused by then, but all the same I never saw a man die in a more hallowed sort of calm.

Once, during the malaria season in the Eastern Transvaal, it seemed to me, when I was in a high fever and like to die, that the whole world was a big burial-ground. I thought it was the earth itself that was a graveyard, and not just those little fenced-in bits of land dotted with tombstones, in the shade of a Western Province oak tree or by the side of a Transvaal koppie. This was a nightmare that worried me a great deal, and so I was very glad, when I recovered from the fever, to think that we Boers had properly marked-out places on our farms for white people to be laid to rest in, in a civilized Christian way, instead of having to be buried just anyhow, along with a dead wild-cat, maybe, or a Bushman with a clay-pot, and things.

When I mentioned this to my friend, Stoffel Oosthuizen, who was in the Low Country with me at the time, he agreed with me wholeheartedly. There were people who talked in a high-flown way of death as the great leveller, he said, and those high-flown people also declared that everyone was made kin by death. He would still like to see those things proved, Stoffel Oosthuizen said. After all, that was one of the reasons why the Boers trekked away into the Transvaal and the Free State, he said, because the British government wanted to give the vote to any Cape Coloured person walking about with a kroes head and big cracks in his feet.

The first time he heard that sort of talk about death coming to all of us alike, and making us all equal, Stoffel Oosthuizen's suspicions were aroused. It sounded like out of a speech made by one of those liberal Cape politicians, he explained.

I found something very comforting in Stoffel Oosthuizen's words.

Then, to illustrate his contention, Stoffel Oosthuizen told me a story of an incident that took place in a bygone Transvaal kaffir war. I don't know whether he told the story incorrectly, or whether it was just that kind of a story, but, by the time he had finished, all my uncertainties had, I discovered, come back to me.

'You can go and look at Hans Welman's tombstone any time you are at Nietverdiend,' Stoffel Oosthuizen said. 'The slab of red sandstone is weathered by now, of course, seeing how long ago it all happened. But the inscription is still legible. I was with Hans Welman on that morning when he fell. Our commando had been ambushed by the kaffirs and was retreating. I could do nothing for Hans Welman. Once, when I looked round, I saw a tall kaffir bending over him and plunging an assegai into him. Shortly afterwards I saw the kaffir stripping the clothes off Hans Welman. A yellow kaffir dog was yelping excitedly around his black master. Although I was in grave danger myself, with several dozen kaffirs making straight for me on foot through the bush, the fury I felt at the sight of what that tall kaffir was doing made me hazard a last shot. Reining in my horse, and taking what aim I could under the circumstances, I pressed the trigger. My luck was in. I saw the kaffir fall forward beside the naked body of Hans Welman. Then I set spurs to my horse and galloped off at full speed, with the foremost of my pursuers already almost upon me. The last I saw was that yellow dog bounding up to his master – whom I had wounded mortally, as we were to discover later.

'As you know, that kaffir war dragged on for a long time. There were few pitched battles. Mainly, what took place were bush skirmishes, like the one in which Hans Welman lost his life.

'After about six months, quiet of a sort was restored to the Marico and Zoutpansberg districts. Then the day came when I went out, in company of a handful of other burghers, to fetch in the remains of Hans Welman, at his widow's request, for burial in the little cemetery plot on the farm. We took a coffin with us on a Cape cart.

'We located the scene of the skirmish without difficulty. Indeed, Hans Welman had been killed not very far from his own farm, which had been temporarily abandoned, together with the other farms in that part, during the time that the trouble with the kaffirs had lasted. We drove up to the spot where I remembered having seen Hans Welman lying dead on the ground, with the tall kaffir next to him. From a distance I again saw that yellow dog. He slipped away into the bush at our approach. I could not help feeling that there was something rather stirring about that beast's fidelity, even though it was bestowed on a dead kaffir.

'We were now confronted with a queer situation. We found that what was left of Hans Welman and the kaffir consisted of little more than pieces of sun-dried flesh and the dismembered fragments of bleached skeletons. The sun and wild animals and birds of prey had done their work. There was a heap of human bones, with here and there leathery strips of blackened flesh. But we could not tell which was the white man and which the kaffir. To make it still more confusing, a lot of bones were missing altogether, having no doubt been dragged away by wild animals into their lairs in the bush. Another thing was that Hans Welman and that kaffir had been just about the same size.'

Stoffel Oosthuizen paused in his narrative, and I let my imagination dwell for a moment on that situation. And I realized just how those Boers must have felt about it: about the thought of bringing the remains of a Transvaal burgher home to his widow for Christian burial, and perhaps having a lot of kaffir bones mixed up with the burgher – lying with him in the same tomb on which the mauve petals from the oleander overhead would fall.

'I remember one of our party saying that that was the worst of these kaffir wars,' Stoffel Oosthuizen continued. 'If it had been a war against the English, and part of a dead Englishman had got lifted into that coffin by mistake, it wouldn't have mattered so much, he said.'

There seemed to me in this story to be something as strange as the African veld.

Stoffel Oosthuizen said that the little party of Boers spent almost a whole afternoon with the remains in order to try to get the white man sorted out from the kaffir. By the evening they had laid all they could find of what seemed like Hans Welman's bones in the coffin in the Cape cart. The rest of the bones and flesh they buried on the spot.

Stoffel Oosthuizen added that, no matter what the difference in the colour of their skin had been, it was impossible to say that the kaffir's bones were less white than Hans Welman's. Nor was it possible to say that the kaffir's sun-dried flesh was any blacker than the white man's. Alive, you couldn't go wrong in distinguishing between a white man and a kaffir. Dead, you had great difficulty in telling them apart.

'Naturally, we burghers felt very bitter about this whole affair,'

Stoffel Oosthuizen said, 'and our resentment was something that we couldn't explain, quite. Afterwards, several other men who were there that day told me that they had the same feelings of suppressed anger that I did. They wanted somebody – just once – to make a remark such as "in death they were not divided". Then you would have seen an outburst, all right. Nobody did say anything like that, however. We all knew better. Two days later a funeral service was conducted in the little cemetery on the Welman farm, and shortly afterwards the sandstone memorial was erected that you can still see there.'

That was the story Stoffel Oosthuizen told me after I had recovered from the fever. It was a story that, as I have said, had in it features as strange as the African veld. But it brought me no peace in my broodings after that attack of malaria. Especially when Christoffel Oosthuizen spoke of how he had occasion, one clear night when the stars shone, to pass that quiet graveyard on the Welman farm. Something leapt up from the mound beside the sandstone slab. It gave him quite a turn, Stoffel Oosthuizen said, for the third time – and in that way – to come across that yellow kaffir dog.

Funeral Earth

We had a difficult task, that time (Oom Schalk Lourens said), teaching Sijefu's tribe of Mtosas to become civilized. But they did not show any appreciation. Even after we had set fire to their huts in a long row round the slopes of Abjaterskop, so that you could see the smoke almost as far as Nietverdiend, the Mtosas remained just about as unenlightened as ever. They would retreat into the mountains, where it was almost impossible for our commando to follow them on horseback. They remained hidden in the thick bush.

'I can sense these kaffirs all around us,' Veld-kornet Andries Joubert said to our seksie of about a dozen burghers when we had come to a halt in a clearing amid the tall withaaks. 'I have been in so many kaffir wars that I can almost *smell* when there are kaffirs lying in wait for us with assegais. And yet all day long you never see a single Mtosa that you can put a lead bullet through.'

He also said that if this war went on much longer we would forget altogether how to handle a gun. And what would we do then, when we again had to fight England?

Young Fanie Louw, who liked saying funny things, threw back his head and pretended to be sniffing the air with discrimination. 'I can smell a whole row of assegais with broad blades and short handles,' Fanie Louw said. 'The stabbing assegai has got more of a selon's rose sort of smell about it than a throwing spear. The selon's rose that you come across in graveyards.'

The veld-kornet did not think Fanie Louw's remark very funny, however. And he said we all knew that this was the first time Fanie Louw had ever been on commando. He also said that if a crowd of Mtosas were to leap out of the bush on to us suddenly, then you wouldn't be able to smell Fanie Louw for dust. The veld-kornet also said another thing that was even better.

Our group of burghers laughed heartily. Maybe Veld-kornet Joubert could not think out a lot of nonsense to say just on the spur of the moment, in the way that Fanie Louw could, but give our veld-kornet a chance to reflect, first, and he would come out with the kind of remark that you just had to admire.

Indeed, from the very next thing Veld-kornet Joubert said, you could see how deep was his insight. And he did not have to think much, either, then.

'Let us get out of here as quick as hell, men,' he said, speaking very distinctly. 'Perhaps the kaffirs are hiding out in the open turf lands, where there are no trees. And none of this long tamboekie grass, either.'

When we emerged from that stretch of bush we were glad to discover that our veld-kornet had been right, like always.

For another group of Transvaal burghers had hit on the same strategy.

'We were in the middle of the bush,' their leader, Combrinck, said to us, after we had exchanged greetings. 'A very thick part of the bush, with withaaks standing up like skeletons. And we suddenly thought the Mtosas might have gone into hiding out here in the open.'

You could see that Veld-kornet Joubert was pleased to think that he had, on his own, worked out the same tactics as Combrinck, who was known as a skilful kaffir-fighter. All the same, it seemed as though this was going to be a long war.

It was then that, again speaking out of his turn, Fanie Louw said that all we needed now was for the commandant himself to arrive there in the middle of the turf lands with the main body of burghers. 'Maybe we should even go back to Pretoria to see if the Mtosas aren't perhaps hiding in the Volksraad,' he said. 'Passing laws and things. You know how cheeky a Mtosa is.'

'It can't be worse than some of the laws that the Volksraad is already passing now,' Combrinck said, gruffly. From that we could see that why he had not himself been appointed commandant was because he had voted against the president in the last elections.

By that time the sun was sitting not more than about two Cape feet above a tall koppie on the horizon. Accordingly, we started looking about for a place to camp. It was muddy in the turf lands, and there was no firewood there, but we all said that we did not mind. We would not pamper ourselves by going to sleep in the thick bush, we told one another. It was war time, and we were on commando, and the mud of the turf lands was good enough for *us*, we said.

It was then that an unusual thing happened.

For we suddenly did see Mtosas. We saw them from a long way off. They came out of the bush and marched right out into the open. They made no attempt to hide. We saw in amazement that they were coming straight in our direction, advancing in single file. And we observed, even from that distance, that they were unarmed. Instead of assegais and shields they carried burdens on their heads. And almost in that same moment we realized, from the heavy look of those burdens, that the carriers must be women.

For that reason we took our guns in our hands and stood waiting. Since it was women, we were naturally prepared for the lowest form of treachery.

As the column drew nearer we saw that at the head of it was Ndambe, an old Native whom we knew well. For years he had been Sijefu's chief counsellor. Ndambe held up his hand. The line of women halted. Ndambe spoke. He declared that we white men were kings among kings and elephants among elephants. He also said that we were ringhals snakes more poisonous and generally disgusting than any ringhals snake in the country.

We knew, of course, that Ndambe was only paying us compliments in his ignorant Mtosa fashion. And so we naturally felt highly gratified. I can still remember the way Jurie Bekker nudged me in the ribs and said, 'Did you hear that?'

When Ndambe went on, however, to say that we were filthier than the spittle of a green tree-toad, several burghers grew restive. They felt that there was perhaps such a thing as carrying these tribal courtesies a bit too far.

It was then that Veld-kornet Joubert, slipping his finger inside the trigger guard of his gun, requested Ndambe to come to the point. By the expression on our veld-kornet's face, you could see that he had had enough of compliments for one day.

They had come to offer peace, Ndambe told us then.

What the women carried on their heads were presents.

At a sign from Ndambe the column knelt in the mud of the turf land. They brought lion and zebra skins and elephant tusks, and beads and brass bangles and, on a long grass mat, the whole haunch of a red Afrikaner ox, hide and hoof and all. And several pigs cut in half. And clay pots filled to the brim with white beer, and also – and this we prized most – witchdoctor medicines that protected you against goël spirits at night and the evil eye.

Ndambe gave another signal. A woman with a clay pot on her head rose up from the kneeling column and advanced towards us. We saw then that what she had in the pot was black earth. It was wet and almost like turf soil. We couldn't understand what they wanted to bring us that for. As though we didn't have enough of it, right there where we were standing, and sticking to our veldskoens, and all. And yet Ndambe acted as though that was the most precious part of the peace offerings that his chief, Sijefu, had sent us.

It was when Ndambe spoke again that we saw how ignorant he and his chief and the whole Mtosa tribe were, really.

He took a handful of soil out of the pot and pressed it together between his fingers. Then he told us how honoured the Mtosa tribe was because we were waging war against them. In the past they had only had flat-faced Mshangaans with spiked knobkerries to fight against, he said, but now it was different. Our veld-kornet took half a step forward, then, in case Ndambe was going to start flattering us again. So Ndambe said, simply, that the Mtosas would be glad if we came and made war against them later on, when the harvests had been gathered in. But in the meantime the tribe did not wish to continue fighting.

It was the time for sowing.

Ndambe let the soil run through his fingers, to show us how good it was. He also invited us to taste it. We declined.

We accepted the presents and peace was made. And I can still remember how Veld-kornet Joubert shook his head and said, 'Can you beat the Mtosas for ignorance?'

And I can still remember what Jurie Bekker said, also. That was when something made him examine the haunch of beef more closely, and he found his own brand mark on it.

It was not long afterwards that the war came against England.

By the end of the second year of the war the Boer forces were in a very bad way. But we would not make peace. Veld-kornet Joubert was now promoted to commandant. Combrinck fell in the battle before Dalmanutha. Jurie Bekker was still with us. And so was Fanie Louw. And it was strange how attached we had grown to Fanie Louw during the years of hardship that we went through together in the field. But up to the end we had to admit that, while we had got used to his jokes, and we knew there was no harm in them, we would have preferred it that he should stop making them.

He did stop, and for ever, in a skirmish near a block-house. We buried him in the shade of a thorn-tree. We got ready to fill in his grave, after which the commandant would say a few words and we would bare our heads and sing a psalm. As you know, it was customary at a funeral for each mourner to take up a handful of earth and fling it in the grave.

When Commandant Joubert stooped down and picked up his handful of earth, a strange thing happened. And I remembered that other war, against the Mtosas. And we knew – although we would not say it – what was now that longing in the hearts of each of us. For Commandant Joubert did not straightway drop the soil into Fanie Louw's grave. Instead, he kneaded the damp ground between his fingers. It was as though he had forgotten that it was funeral earth. He seemed to be thinking not of death, then, but of life.

We patterned after him, picking up handfuls of soil and pressing it together. We felt the deep loam in it, and saw how springy it was, and we let it trickle through our fingers. And we could remember only that it was the time for sowing.

I understood then how, in an earlier war, the Mtosas had felt, they who were also farmers.

The Mafeking Road

When people ask me – as they often do – how it is that I can tell the best stories of anybody in the Transvaal (Oom Schalk Lourens said, modestly), then I explain to them that I just learn through observing the way that the world has with men and women. When I say this they nod their heads wisely, and say that they understand, and I nod my head wisely also, and that seems to satisfy them. But the thing I say to them is a lie, of course.

For it is not the story that counts. What matters is the way you tell it. The important thing is to know just at what moment you must knock out your pipe on your veldskoen, and at what stage of the story you must start talking about the School Committee at Drogevlei. Another necessary thing is to know what part of the story to leave out.

And you can never learn these things.

Look at Floris van Barnevelt, for instance. Floris, the last of the Van Barnevelts. There is no doubt that he had a good story, and he should have been able to get people to listen to it. And yet nobody took any notice of him or of the things he had to say. Just because he couldn't tell the story properly.

Accordingly, it made me sad whenever I listened to him talk. For I could tell just where he went wrong. He never knew the moment at which to knock the ash out of his pipe. He always mentioned his opinion of the Drogevlei School Committee in the wrong place. And, what was still worse, he didn't know what part of the story to leave out.

And it was no use my trying to teach him, because as I have said, this is a thing that you can never learn. And so, each time he had told his story, I would see him turn away from me, with a look of doom on his face, and walk slowly down the road, stoop-shouldered, the last of the Van Barnevelts.

On the wall of Floris' voorkamer is a long family tree of the

Van Barnevelts. You can see it there for yourself. It goes back for over two hundred years to the Van Barnevelts of Amsterdam. At one time it went even further back, but that was before the white ants started on the top part of it and ate away quite a lot of Van Barnevelts. Nevertheless, if you look at this list, you will notice that at the bottom, under Floris' own name, there is the last entry, 'Stephanus'. And behind the name, Stephanus, between two bent strokes, you will read the words: 'Obiit Mafeking'.

At the outbreak of the Second Boer War Floris van Barnevelt was a widower, with one son, Stephanus, who was aged seventeen. The commando from our part of the Transvaal set off very cheerfully. We made a fine show, with our horses and our wide hats and our bandoliers, and with the sun shining on the barrels of our Mausers.

Young Stephanus van Barnevelt was the gayest of us all. But he said there was one thing he didn't like about the war, and that was that, in the end, we would have to go over the sea. He said that, after we had invaded the whole of the Cape, our commando would have to go on a ship and invade England also.

But we didn't go overseas, just then. Instead, our veld-kornet told us that the burghers from our part had been ordered to join the big commando that was lying at Mafeking. We had to go and shoot a man there called Baden-Powell.

We rode steadily on into the west. After a while we noticed that our veld-kornet frequently got off his horse and engaged in conversation with passing kaffirs, leading them some distance from the roadside and speaking earnestly to them. Of course, it was right that our veld-kornet should explain to the kaffirs that it was war-time, now, and that the Republic expected every kaffir to stop smoking so much dagga and to think seriously about what was going on. But we noticed that each time at the end of the conversation the kaffir would point towards something, and that our veld-kornet would take much pains to follow the direction of the kaffir's finger.

Of course, we understood, then, what it was all about. Our veld-kornet was a young fellow, and he was shy to let us see that he didn't know the way to Mafeking.

Somehow, after that, we did not have so much confidence in our veld-kornet.

After a few days we got to Mafeking. We stayed there a long while, until the English troops came up and relieved the place. We left, then. We left quickly. The English troops had brought a lot of artillery with them. And if we had difficulty in finding the road to Mafeking, we had no difficulty in finding the road away from Mafeking. And this time our veld-kornet did not need kaffirs, either, to point with their fingers where we had to go. Even though we did a lot of travelling in the night.

Long afterwards I spoke to an Englishman about this. He said it gave him a queer feeling to hear about the other side of the story of Mafeking. He said there had been very great rejoicings in England when Mafeking was relieved, and it was strange to think of the other aspect of it – of a defeated country and of broken columns blundering through the dark.

I remember many things that happened on the way back from Mafeking. There was no moon. And the stars shone down fitfully on the road that was full of guns and frightened horses and desperate men. The veld throbbed with the hoofbeats of baffled commandos. The stars looked down on scenes that told sombrely of a nation's ruin; they looked on the muzzles of the Mausers that had failed the Transvaal for the first time.

Of course, as a burgher of the Republic, I knew what my duty was. And that was to get as far away as I could from the place where, in the sunset, I had last seen the English artillery. The other burghers knew their duty, also. Our commandants and veld-kornets had to give very few orders. Nevertheless, although I rode very fast, there was one young man who rode still faster. He kept ahead of me all the time. He did his duty to the Republic better than I did – by at least a dozen lengths. He rode, as a burgher should ride when there may be stray bullets flying, with his head well down and with his arms almost round the horse's neck.

He was Stephanus, the young son of Floris van Barnevelt.

There was much grumbling and dissatisfaction, some time afterwards, when our leaders started making an effort to get the commandos in order again. In the end they managed to get us to halt. But most of us felt that this was a foolish thing to do. Especially as there was still a lot of firing going on, all over the place, in a haphazard fashion, and we couldn't tell how far the English had followed us in the dark. Furthermore, the commandos had scattered in so many different directions that it seemed hopeless to try and get them together again until after the war.

Stephanus and I dismounted and stood by our horses. Soon there was a large body of men around us. Their figures looked strange and shadowy in the starlight. Some of them stood by their horses. Others sat down on the grass by the roadside. 'Vas staan, burghers, vas staan,' came the commands of our officers. And all the time we could still hear what sounded a lot like lyddite. It seemed foolish to be waiting there.

'The next they'll want,' Stephanus van Barnevelt said, 'is for us to go back to Mafeking. Perhaps our commandant has left his tobacco-pouch behind, there.'

Some of us laughed at this remark, but Floris, who had not dismounted, said that Stephanus ought to be ashamed of himself for talking like that. From what we could see of Floris in the gloom, he looked quite impressive, sitting very straight up in the saddle, with the stars shining on his beard and rifle.

'If the veld-kornet told me to go back to Mafeking,' Floris said, 'I would go back.'

'That's how a burgher should talk,' the veld-kornet said, feeling flattered. For he had had little authority since the time we found out what he was talking to the kaffirs for.

'I wouldn't go back to Mafeking for anybody,' Stephanus replied. 'Unless, maybe, it's to hand myself over to the English.'

'We can shoot you for doing that,' the veld-kornet said. 'It's contrary to military law.'

'I wish I knew something about military law,' Stephanus answered. 'Then I would draw up a peace treaty between Stephanus van Barnevelt and England.'

Some of the men laughed again. But Floris shook his head

sadly. He said that the Van Barnevelts had fought bravely against Spain in a war that lasted eighty years.

Suddenly, out of the darkness, there came a sharp rattle of musketry, and our men started getting uneasy again. But the sound of the firing decided Stephanus. He jumped on his horse quickly.

'I am turning back,' he said, 'I am going to hands-up to the English.'

'No, don't go,' the veld-kornet called to him lamely. 'Or at least wait until the morning. They might shoot you in the dark by mistake.' As I have said, the veld-kornet had very little authority.

Two days passed before we again saw Floris van Barnevelt. He was in a very worn and troubled state, and he said that it had been very hard for him to find his way back to us.

'You should have asked the kaffirs,' one of our number said with a laugh. 'All the kaffirs know our veld-kornet.'

But Floris did not speak about what happened that night, when we saw him riding out under the starlight, following after his son and shouting to him to be a man and to fight for his country. Also, Floris did not mention Stephanus again, his son who was not worthy to be a Van Barnevelt.

After that we got separated. Our veld-kornet was the first to be taken prisoner. And I often thought that he must feel very lonely on St Helena. Because there were no kaffirs from whom he could ask the way out of the barbed-wire camp.

Then, at last, our leaders came together at Vereeniging, and peace was made. And we returned to our farms, relieved that the war was over, but with heavy hearts at the thought that it had all been for nothing, and that over the Transvaal veld the vierkleur would not wave again.

And Floris van Barnevelt put back in its place, on the wall of the voorkamer, the copy of his family tree that he had carried with him in his knapsack throughout the war. Then a new schoolmaster came to this part of the Marico, and after a long talk with Floris the schoolmaster wrote, behind Stephanus' name, between two curved lines, the words that you can still read there: 'Obiit Mafeking'.

Consequently, if you ask any person hereabouts what 'obiit' means, he is able to tell you, right away, that it is a foreign word, and that it means to ride up to the English, holding your Mauser in the air, with a white flag tied on it, near the muzzle.

But it was only long afterwards that Floris van Barnevelt started telling his story.

And then they took no notice of him. And they wouldn't allow him to be nominated for the Drogevlei School Committee, on the grounds that a man must be wrong in the head to talk in such an irresponsible fashion.

But I knew that Floris had a good story, and that its only fault was that he told it badly. He mentioned the Drogevlei School Committee too soon. And he knocked the ash out of his pipe in the wrong place. And he always insisted on telling that part of the story that he should have left out.

Karel Flysman

It was after the English had taken Pretoria that I first met Karel Flysman (Oom Schalk Lourens said).

Karel was about twenty-five. He was a very tall, well-built young man with a red face and curly hair. He was good-looking, and while I was satisfied with what the good Lord had done for me, yet I felt sometimes that if only He had given me a body like what Karel Flysman had got, I would go to church oftener and put more in the collection plate.

When the big commandos broke up, we separated into small companies, so that the English would not be able to catch all the Republican forces at the same time. If we were few and scattered the English would have to look harder to find us in the dongas and bushes and rante. And the English, at the beginning, moved slowly. When their scouts saw us making coffee under the trees by the side of the spruit, where it was cool and pleasant, they turned back to the main army and told their general about us. The general would look through his field-glasses and nod his head a few times.

'Yes,' he would say, 'that is the enemy. I can see them under those trees. There's that man with the long beard eating out of a pot with his hands. Why doesn't he use a knife and fork? I don't think he can be a gentleman. Bring out the maps and we'll attack them.'

Then the general and a few of his commandants would get together and work it all out.

'This cross I put here will be those trees,' the general would say. 'This crooked line I am drawing here is the spruit, and this circle will stand for the pot that that man is eating out of with his fingers . . . No, that's no good, now. They've moved the pot. Wonderful how crafty these Boers are.'

Anyway, they would work out the plans of our position for

half an hour, and at the end of that time they would find out that they had got it all wrong. Because they had been using a map of the Rustenburg District, and actually they were half-way into the Marico. So by the time they had everything ready to attack us, we had already moved off and were making coffee under some other trees.

How do I know all these things? Well, I went right through the Boer War, and I was only once caught. And that was when our commandant, Apie Terblanche, led us through the Bushveld by following some maps that he had captured from the British. But Apie Terblanche never was much use. He couldn't even hang a Hottentot properly.

As I was saying, Karel Flysman first joined up with our commando when we were trekking through the Bushveld north of the railway line from Mafeking to Barberton. It seemed that he had got separated from his commando and that he had been wandering about through the bush for some days before he came across us. He was mounted on a big black horse and, as he rode well, even for a Boer, he was certainly the finest-looking burgher I had seen for a long time.

One afternoon, when we had been in the saddle since before sunrise, and had also been riding hard the day before, we off-saddled at the foot of a koppie, where the bush was high and thick. We were very tired. A British column had come across us near the Malopo River. The meeting was a surprise for the British as well as for us. We fought for about an hour, but the fire was so heavy that we had to retreat, leaving behind us close on to a dozen men, including the veld-kornet. Karel Flysman displayed great promptitude and decision. As soon as the first shot was fired he jumped off his horse and threw down his rifle; he crawled away from the enemy on his hands and knees. He crawled very quickly too. An hour later, when we had ourselves given up resisting the English, we came across him in some long grass about a mile away from where the fighting had been. He was still crawling.

Karel Flysman's horse had remained with the rest of the horses, and it was just by good luck that Karel was able to get into the saddle and take to flight with us before the English got too close.

We were pursued for a considerable distance. It didn't seem as though we would ever be able to shake off the enemy. I suppose that the reason they followed us so well was because that column could not have been in charge of a general; their leader must have been only a kaptein or a commandant, who probably did not understand how to use a map.

It was towards the afternoon that we discovered that the English were no longer hanging on to our rear. When we dismounted in the thick bush at the foot of the koppie, it was all we could do to unsaddle our horses. Then we lay down on the grass and stretched out our limbs and turned round to get comfortable, but we were so fatigued that it was a long time before we could get into restful positions.

Even then we couldn't get to sleep. The commandant called us together and selected a number of burghers who were to form a committee to try Karel Flysman for running away. There wasn't much to be said about it. Karel Flysman was young, but at the same time he was old enough to know better. An ordinary burgher has got no right to run away from a fight at the head of the commando. It is the general's place to run away first. As a member of this committee I was at pains to point all this out to the prisoner.

We were seated in a circle on the grass. Karel Flysman stood in the centre. He was bare-headed. His Mauser and bandolier had been taken away from him. His trousers were muddy and broken at the knees from the way in which he had crawled that long distance through the grass. There was also mud on his face. But in spite of all that, there was a fine, manly look about him, and I am sure that others besides myself felt sorry that Karel Flysman should be so much of a coward.

We were sorry for him, in a way. We were also tired, so that we didn't feel like getting up and doing any more shooting. Accordingly we decided that if the commandant warned him about it we would give him one more chance.

'You have heard what your fellow burghers have decided about you,' the commandant said. 'Let this be a lesson to you. A burgher of the Republic who runs away quickly may rise to be commandant. But a burgher of the Republic must also know that there is a time to fight. And it is better to be shot by the English than by your own people, even though,' the commandant added, 'the English can't shoot straight.'

So we gave Karel Flysman back his rifle and bandolier, and we went to sleep. We didn't even trouble to put out guards round the camp. It would not have been any use putting out pickets, for they would have been sure to fall asleep, and if the English did come during the night they would know of our whereabouts by falling over our pickets.

As it happened, that night the English came.

The first thing I knew about it was when a man put his foot on my face. He put it on heavily, too, and by the feel of it I could tell that his veldskoens were made of unusually hard ox-hide. In those days, through always being on the alert for the enemy, I was a light sleeper, and that man's boot on my face woke me up without any difficulty. In the darkness I swore at him and he cursed back at me, saying something about the English. So we carried on for a few moments; he spoke about the English; I spoke about my face.

Then I heard the commandant's voice, shouting out orders for us to stand to arms. I got my rifle and found my way to a sloot where our men were gathering for the fight. Up to that moment it had been too dark for me to distinguish anything that was more than a few feet away from me. But just then the clouds drifted away, and the moon shone down on us. It happened so quickly that for a brief while I was almost afraid. Everything that had been black before suddenly stood out pale and ghostly. The trees became silver with dark shadows in them, and it was among these shadows that we strove to see the English. Wherever a branch rustled in the wind or a twig moved, we thought we could see soldiers. Then somebody fired a shot. At once the firing became general.

I had been in many fights before, so that there was nothing new to me in the rattle of Mausers and Lee-Metfords, and in the red spurts of flame that suddenly broke out all round us. We could see little of the English. That meant that they could see even less of us.

All we had to aim at were those spurts of flame. We realized quickly that it was only an advance party of the English that we had up against us; it was all rifle fire; the artillery would be coming along behind the main body. What we had to do was to go on shooting a little longer and then slip away before the rest of the English came. Near me a man shouted that he was hit. Many more were hit that night.

I bent down to put another cartridge-clip into my magazine, when I noticed a man lying flat in the sloot, with his arms about his head. His gun lay on the grass in front of him. By his dress and the size of his body I knew it was Karel Flysman. I didn't know whether it was a bullet or cowardice that had brought him down in that way. Therefore, to find out, I trod on his face. He shouted out something about the English, whereupon (as he used the same words) I was satisfied that he was the man who had awakened me with his boot before the fight started. I put some more of my weight on to the foot that was on his face.

'Don't do that. Oh, don't,' Karel Flysman shouted. 'I am dying. Oh, I am sure I am dying. The English . . .'

I stooped down and examined him. He was unwounded. All that was wrong with him was his spirit.

'God,' I said, 'why can't you try to be a man, Karel? If you've got to be shot nothing can stop the bullet, whether you are afraid or whether you're not. To see the way you're lying down there anybody would think that you are at least the commandant-general.'

He blurted out a lot of things, but he spoke so rapidly and his lips trembled so much that I couldn't understand much of what he said. And I didn't want to understand him, either. I kicked him in the ribs and told him to take his rifle and fight, or I would shoot him as he lay. But of course all that was of no use. He was actually so afraid of the enemy that even if he knew for sure that I was going to shoot him he would just have lain down where he was and have waited for the bullet.

In the meantime the fire of the enemy had grown steadier, so that we knew that at any moment we could expect the order to retreat.

'In a few minutes you can get back to your old game of running,' I shouted to Karel Flysman, but I don't think he heard much of what I said, on account of the continuous rattle of the rifles.

But he must have heard the word 'running'.

'I can't,' he cried. 'My legs are too weak. I am dying.'

He went on like that some more. He also mentioned a girl's name. He repeated it several times. I think the name was Francina. He shouted out the name and cried out that he didn't want to die. Then a whistle blew, and shortly afterwards we got the order to prepare for the retreat.

I did my best to help Karel out of the sloot. The Englishmen would have laughed if they could have seen that struggle in the moonlight. But the affair didn't last too long. Karel suddenly collapsed back into the sloot and lay still. That time it was a bullet. Karel Flysman was dead.

Often after I have thought of Karel Flysman and of the way he died. I have also thought of that girl he spoke about. Perhaps she thinks of her lover as a hero who laid down his life for his country. And perhaps it is as well that she should think that.

The Question

Stefanus Malherbe had difficulty in getting access to the president, to put to him the question of which we were all anxious to learn the answer.

It was at Waterval Onder and President Kruger was making preparations to leave for Europe to enlist the help of foreign countries in the Transvaal's struggle against England. General Louis Botha had just been defeated at Dalmanutha. Accordingly we who were the last of the Boer commandos in the field found ourselves hemmed in against the Portuguese border by the British forces, the few miles of railway line from Nelspruit to Komatipoort being all that still remained to us of Transvaal soil. The Boer War had hardly begun and it already looked like the end.

But when we had occasion to watch from a considerable distance a column of British dragoons advancing through a half-mile stretch of bush country, there were those of us who realized that the Boer War might, after all, not be over yet. It took the column two hours to get through that bush.

Although we who served under Veld-kornet Stefanus Malherbe were appointed to the duty of guarding President Kruger during those last days, we had neither the opportunity nor the temerity to talk to him in that house at Waterval Onder. For one thing there were those men with big stomachs and heavy gold watch-chains all crowding around the president with papers they wanted him to sign. Nevertheless, when the news came that the English had broken through at Dalmanutha we overheard some of those men say, not raising their voices unduly, that something or other was no longer worth the paper it was written on. Next morning, when President Kruger again came on the front stoep of the house, alone this time, we were for the first time able to see him clearly instead of through the thick screen of grey smoke being blown into his face from imported cigars.

'Well,' Thys Haasbroek said, 'I hope the president when he gets to Europe enlists the right kind of foreigners to come and fight for the Republic. It would be too bad if he came back with another crowd of uitlanders with big stomachs and watch-chains, waving papers for concessions.'

I mention this remark made by one of the burghers at Waterval Onder with the president to show you that there was not a uniform spirit of bitter-end loyalty animating the three thousand men who saw day by day the net of the enemy getting more tightly drawn around them. Indeed, speaking for myself, I must confess that the enthusiasm of those of our leaders who at intervals addressed us, exhorting us to courage, had but a restricted influence on my mind.

Especially when the orders came for the rolling stock to be dynamited.

For we had brought with us, in our retreat from Magersfontein, practically all the carriages and engines and trucks of the Transvaal and Orange Free State railways. At first we were much saddened by the necessity for destroying the property of our country. But afterwards something got into our blood which made it all seem like a good joke. I know that our own little group that was under the leadership of Veld-kornet Stefanus Malherbe really derived a considerable amount of enjoyment, towards the end, out of blowing railway engines and whole trains into the air. A couple of former shunters who were on commando with us would say things like, 'There goes the Cape mail via Fourteen Streams,' and we would fling ourselves into a ditch to escape the flying fragments of wood and steel. One of them also used to shout, 'All seats for Bloemfontein,' or 'First stop Elandsfontein,' after the fuse was lit and he would blow his whistle and wave a green flag. For several days it seemed that between Nelspruit and Hectorspruit you couldn't look up at any part of the sky without seeing wheels in it.

And during all this time we treated the whole affair as fun and the former shunters had got to calling out, 'There goes the nine-twenty to De Aar,' against the signals and, 'There's a girl with fair hair travelling by herself in the end compartment.' Being railwaymen, they couldn't think of anything else to say.

Because the war of the big commandos, and of men like Generals Joubert and Cronjé, was over it seemed to us that all the fighting was just about done. We did not know that the Boer War of General de Wet and Ben Viljoen and General Muller was then only about to begin.

The next order that our veld-kornet, Stefanus Malherbe, brought us from the commandant was for the destruction of our stores and field guns and ammunition dumps as well. All we had to retain were our Mausers and horses, the order said. That did not give us much cause for hope. At the same time the first of General Louis Botha's burghers from the Dalmanutha fight began to arrive in our camp. They were worn out from their long retreat and many of them had acquired the singular habit of looking round over their shoulders very quickly, every so often, right in the middle of a conversation. Their presence did not help to inspire us with military ardour. One of these burghers was very upset at our having blown up all the trains. He had been born and bred in the gramadoelas and had been looking forward to his first journey by rail.

'I just wanted to feel how the thing rides,' he said in disappointed tones, in between trying to wipe off stray patches of yellow lyddite stains he had got at Dalmanutha. 'But even if there *was* still another train left I suppose it would be too late, now.'

'Yes, I am sure it would be too late,' I said, also looking quickly over my shoulder. There was something infectious about this habit that Louis Botha's burghers had brought with them.

Actually, of course, it was not yet too late for there was still a train, with the engine and carriages intact, waiting to take the president out of the Transvaal into Portuguese territory. There were also in the Boer ranks men whose loyalty to the Republic never wavered even in the darkest times. It had been a very long retreat from the Northern Cape Province through the Orange Free State and the Transvaal to where we were now shut in near the Komati River. And it had all happened so quickly.

The Boer withdrawal, when once it got under way, had been fast and complete. I found it not a little disconcerting to think that on one day I had seen the president seated in a spider just outside Paardeberg drinking buttermilk and then on another day, only a few months later, I had seen him sitting on the front stoep of a house at Waterval Onder a thousand miles away, drinking brandy. Moreover, he was getting ready to move again.

'If it is only to Europe that he is going, then it is not so bad,' said an older farmer with a long beard who was an ignorant man in many ways, but whose faith had not faltered throughout the retreat. 'I would not have liked our beloved president to have to travel all that way back to the Northern Cape where we started from. He hasn't the strength for so long a journey. I am glad that it is only to Russia that he is going.'

Because he was not demoralized by defeat, as so many of us were, we who listened to this old farmer's words were touched by his simple loyalty. Indeed, the example set by men of his sort had a far greater influence on the course of the war during the difficult period ahead than the speeches that our leaders came round and made to us from time to time.

Certainly we did not feel that the veld-kornet, Stefanus Malherbe, was a tower of strength. We did not dislike him, nor did we distrust him. We only felt, after a peculiar fashion, that he was too much like the same kind of man that we ourselves were. So we did not have overmuch respect for him.

I have said that we ordinary burghers did not have the temerity to approach the president and to talk to him as man to man of the matter that we wanted to know about. And so we hung back a little while Stefanus Malherbe, an officer on whom many weighty responsibilities reposed, put out his chest and strode towards the house to interview the president. 'Put out your stomach,' one of the burghers called out. He was of course thinking of those men who lately had surrounded the president with their papers and watch-chains and cigars.

And then, when Stefanus Malherbe was moving in the direction of the voorkamer where we knew the president to be, and when the rest of the members of our veldkornetskap had drawn itself together in a little knot that stood nervously waiting just off the stoep for the president's reply – I suppose it had to happen that just then a newly appointed general should have decided to treat us to a patriotic talk. Under other circumstances we would have been impressed perhaps but at that point of time, when we had already blown up our trains and stores and ammunition dumps, and had sunk the pieces that remained of the Staat's Artillerie in the Komati River – along with some papers we had captured in earlier battle – we were not an ideal audience.

We stood still, out of politeness, and listened. But all the time we were wondering if the veld-kornet would perhaps be able to slip away at the end of the speech and manage to get in a few words with President Kruger after all. Anyway, I am sure that we took in very little of what the newly appointed general had to say.

In the end the general realized the position, too. We gathered that he had known he was going to get the appointment that day and that he had prepared a speech for the occasion, to deliver before the president and the State Council, but that he had been unable to have his say in the house because of the bustle attendant upon the president's impending departure. Consequently the general delivered his set speech to us, the first group of burghers he encountered on his way out. After he had got us to sing Psalm 83 and had adjured each one of us to humble himself before the Lord, the general explained at great length that if we could perhaps not hope for victory, since victory might be beyond our capacity, we could still hope for a more worthy kind of defeat.

We made no response to his eloquence. We did not sweep our hats upward in a cheer. We did not call out, 'Ou perd!' We were only concerned with the veld-kornet's chances of having a word with the president before it was too late. The general understood, eventually, that our hearts were not in his address and so he concluded his speech rather abruptly. 'Some defeats are greater than victories,' he said, and he paused for a little while to survey us before adding, 'but not this one, I think.'

The meeting having ended suddenly like that, Veld-kornet Stefanus Malherbe did, after all, manage to get into the voorkamer to speak to President Kruger alone. That much we knew.

But when he came out of the house, the veld-kornet was silent about his conversation with the president. He did not tell us what the president had said in answer to his question. And in the next advance of the English, which was made within that weekend and which took them right into Komatipoort, Veld-kornet Stefanus Malherbe was killed. So he never told us what the president had said in answer to his question about the Kruger millions.

The Rooinek

Rooineks (said Oom Schalk Lourens) are queer. For instance, there was that day when my nephew Hannes and I had dealings with a couple of Englishmen near Dewetsdorp. It was shortly after Sanna's Post, and Hannes and I were lying behind a rock watching the road. Hannes spent odd moments like that in what he called a useful way. He would file the points of his Mauser cartridges on a piece of flat stone until the lead showed through the steel, in that way making them into dum-dum bullets.

I often spoke to my nephew Hannes about that.

'Hannes,' I used to say. 'That is a sin. The Lord is looking at you.'

'That's all right,' Hannes replied. 'The Lord knows that this is the Boer War, and in war-time He will always forgive a little foolishness like this, especially as the English are so many.'

Anyway, as we lay behind that rock we saw, far down the road, two horsemen come galloping up. We remained perfectly still and let them approach to within four hundred paces. They were English officers. They were mounted on first-rate horses and their uniforms looked very fine and smart. They were the most stylish-looking men I had seen for some time, and I felt quite ashamed of my own ragged trousers and veldskoens. I was glad that I was behind a rock and they couldn't see me. Especially as my jacket was also torn all the way down the back, as a result of my having had, three days before, to get through a barbed-wire fence rather quickly. I just got through in time, too. The veld-kornet, who was a fat man and couldn't run so fast, was about twenty yards behind me. And he remained on the wire with a bullet through him. All through the Boer War I was pleased that I was thin and never troubled with corns.

Hannes and I fired just about the same time. One of the officers fell off his horse. He struck the road with his shoulders and rolled over twice, kicking up the red dust as he turned. Then the other soldier did a queer thing. He drew up his horse and got off. He gave just one look in our direction. Then he led his horse up to where the other man was twisting and struggling on the ground. It took him a little while to lift him on to his horse, for it is no easy matter to pick up a man like that when he is helpless. And he did all this slowly and calmly, as though he was not concerned about the fact that the men who had shot his friend were lying only a few hundred yards away. He managed in some way to support the wounded man across the saddle, and walked on beside the horse. After going a few yards he stopped and seemed to remember something. He turned round and waved at the spot where he imagined we were hiding, as though inviting us to shoot. During all that time I had simply lain watching him, astonished at his coolness.

But when he waved his hand I thrust another cartridge into the breach of my Martini and aimed. At that distance I couldn't miss. I aimed very carefully and was just on the point of pulling the trigger when Hannes put his hand on the barrel and pushed up my rifle.

'Don't shoot, Oom Schalk,' he said. 'That's a brave man.'

I looked at Hannes in surprise. His face was very white. I said nothing, and allowed my rifle to sink down on to the grass, but I couldn't understand what had come over my nephew. It seemed that not only was that Englishman queer, but that Hannes was also queer. That's all nonsense not killing a man just because he's brave. If he's a brave man and he's fighting on the wrong side, that's all the more reason to shoot him.

I was with my nephew Hannes for another few months after that. Then one day, in a skirmish near the Vaal River, Hannes with a few dozen other burghers was cut off from the commando and had to surrender. That was the last I ever saw of him. I heard later on that, after taking him prisoner, the English searched Hannes and found dum-dum bullets in his possession. They shot him for that. I was very much grieved when I heard of Hannes' death. He had always been full of life and high spirits. Perhaps Hannes was right in saying that the Lord didn't mind about a little foolishness like dum-dum bullets. But the mistake he made was in forgetting that the English did mind.

I was in the veld until they made peace. Then we laid down our rifles and went home. What I knew my farm by was the hole under the koppie where I quarried slate-stones for the threshing-floor. That was about all that remained as I left it. Everything else was gone. My home was burnt down. My lands were laid waste. My cattle and sheep were slaughtered. Even the stones I had piled for the kraals were pulled down. My wife came out of the concentration camp and we went together to look at our old farm. My wife had gone into the concentration camp with our two children, but she came out alone. And when I saw her again and noticed the way she had changed, I knew that I, who had been through all the fighting, had not seen the Boer War.

Neither Sannie nor I had the heart to go on farming again on that same place. It would be different without the children playing about the house and getting into mischief. We got paid out some money by the new government for part of our losses. So I bought a waggon and oxen and we left the Free State, which was not even the Free State any longer. It was now called the Orange River Colony.

We trekked right through the Transvaal into the northern part of the Marico Bushveld. Years ago, as a boy, I had trekked through that same country with my parents. Now that I went there again I felt that it was still a good country. It was on the far side of the Dwarsberge, near Derdepoort, that we got a government farm. Afterwards other farmers trekked in there as well. One or two of them had also come from the Free State, and I knew them. There were also a few Cape rebels whom I had seen on commando. All of us had lost relatives in the war. Some had died in the concentration camps or on the battlefield. Others had been shot for going into rebellion. So, taken all in all, we who had trekked into that part of the Marico that lay nearest the Bechuanaland border were very bitter against the English.

Then it was that the rooinek came.

It was in the first year of our having settled around Derdepoort. We heard that an Englishman had bought a farm next to

Gerhardus Grobbelaar. This was when we were sitting in the voorkamer of Willem Odendaal's house, which was used as a post office. Once a week the post-cart came up with letters from Zeerust, and we came together at Willem Odendaal's house and talked and smoked and drank coffee. Very few of us ever got letters, and then it was mostly demands to pay for the boreholes that had been drilled on our farms or for cement and fencing materials. But every week regularly we went for the post. Sometimes the post-cart didn't come, because the Groen River was in flood, and we would most of us have gone home without noticing it, if somebody didn't speak about it.

When Koos Steyn heard that an Englishman was coming to live among us he got up from the riempies bank.

'No, kêrels,' he said. 'Always when the Englishman comes, it means that a little later the Boer has got to shift. I'll pack up my waggon and make coffee, and just trek first thing tomorrow morning.'

Most of us laughed then. Koos Steyn often said funny things like that. But some didn't laugh. Somehow, there seemed to be too much truth in Koos Steyn's words.

We discussed the matter and decided that if we Boers in the Marico could help it the rooinek would not stay among us too long. About half an hour later one of Willem Odendaal's children came in and said that there was a strange waggon coming along the big road. We went to the door and looked out. As the waggon came nearer we saw that it was piled up with all kinds of furniture and also sheets of iron and farming implements. There was so much stuff on the waggon that the tent had to be taken off to get everything on.

The waggon rolled along and came to a stop in front of the house. With the waggon there were one white man and two kaffirs. The white man shouted something to the kaffirs and threw down the whip. Then he walked up to where we were standing. He was dressed just as we were, in shirt and trousers and veldskoens, and he had dust all over him. But when he stepped over a thorn-bush we saw that he had got socks on. Therefore we knew that he was an Englishman.

Koos Steyn was standing in front of the door.

The Englishman went up to him and held out his hand.

'Good afternoon,' he said in Afrikaans. 'My name is Webber.'

Koos shook hands with him.

'My name is Prince Lord Alfred Milner,' Koos Steyn said.

That was when Lord Milner was Governor of the Transvaal, and we all laughed. The rooinek also laughed.

'Well, Lord Prince,' he said, 'I can speak your language a little, and I hope that later on I'll be able to speak it better. I'm coming to live here, and I hope that we'll all be friends.'

He then came round to all of us, but the others turned away and refused to shake hands with him. He came up to me last of all; I felt sorry for him, and although his nation had dealt unjustly with my nation, and I had lost both my children in the concentration camp, still it was not so much the fault of this Englishman. It was the fault of the English government, who wanted our gold mines. And it was also the fault of Queen Victoria, who didn't like Oom Paul Kruger, because they say that when he went over to London Oom Paul spoke to her only once for a few minutes. Oom Paul Kruger said that he was a married man and he was afraid of widows.

When the Englishman Webber went back to his waggon Koos Steyn and I walked with him. He told us that he had bought the farm next to Gerhardus Grobbelaar and that he didn't know much about sheep and cattle and mealies, but he had bought a few books on farming, and he was going to learn all he could out of them. When he said that I looked away towards the poort. I didn't want him to see that I was laughing. But with Koos Steyn it was otherwise.

'Man,' he said, 'let me see those books.'

Webber opened the box at the bottom of the waggon and took out about six big books with green covers.

'These are very good books,' Koos Steyn said. 'Yes, they are very good for the white ants. The white ants will eat them all in two nights.'

As I have told you, Koos Steyn was a funny fellow, and no man could help laughing at the things he said.

Those were bad times. There was drought, and we could not sow mealies. The dams dried up, and there was only last year's grass on the veld. We had to pump water out of the boreholes for weeks at a time. Then the rains came and for a while things were better.

Now and again I saw Webber. From what I heard about him it seemed that he was working hard. But of course no rooinek can make a living out of farming, unless they send him money every month from England. And we found out that almost all the money Webber had was what he had paid on the farm. He was always reading in those green books what he had to do. It's lucky that those books are written in English, and that the Boers can't read them. Otherwise many more farmers would be ruined every year. When his cattle had the heart-water, or his sheep had the blue-tongue, or there were cut-worms or stalk-borers in his mealies, Webber would look it all up in his books. I suppose that when the kaffirs stole his sheep he would look that up, too.

Still, Koos Steyn helped Webber quite a lot and taught him a number of things, so that matters did not go as badly with him as they would have if he had only acted according to the lies that were printed in those green books. Webber and Koos Steyn became very friendly. Koos Steyn's wife had had a baby just a few weeks before Webber came. It was the first child they had after being married seven years, and they were very proud of it. It was a girl. Koos Steyn said that he would sooner it had been a boy; but that, even so, it was better than nothing. Right from the first Webber had taken a liking to that child, who was christened Jemima after her mother. Often when I passed Koos Steyn's house I saw the Englishman sitting on the front stoep with the child on his knees.

In the meantime the other farmers around there became annoyed on account of Koos Steyn's friendship with the rooinek. They said that Koos was a handsopper and a traitor to his country. He was intimate with a man who had helped to bring about the downfall of the Afrikaner nation. Yet it was not fair to call Koos a handsopper. Koos had lived in the Graaff-Reinet District when the war broke out, so that he was a Cape Boer and need not have fought. Nevertheless, he joined up with a Free State commando and remained until peace was made, and if at any time the English had caught him they would have shot him as a rebel, in the same way that they shot Scheepers and many others.

Gerhardus Grobbelaar spoke about this once when we were in Willem Odendaal's post office.

'You are not doing right,' Gerhardus said. 'Boer and Englishman have been enemies since before Slagtersnek. We've lost this war, but some day we'll win. It's the duty we owe to our children's children to stand against the rooineks. Remember the concentration camps.'

There seemed to me to be truth in what Gerhardus said.

'But the English are here now, and we've got to live with them,' Koos answered. 'When we get to understand one another perhaps we won't need to fight any more. This Englishman Webber is learning Afrikaans very well, and some day he might almost be one of us. The only thing I can't understand about him is that he has a bath every morning. But if he stops that and if he doesn't brush his teeth any more you will hardly be able to tell him from a Boer.'

Although he made a joke about it, I felt that in what Koos Steyn said there was also truth.

Then, the year after the drought, the miltsiek broke out. The miltsiek seemed to be in the grass of the veld, and in the water of the dams, and even in the air the cattle breathed. All over the place I would find cows and oxen lying dead. We all became very discouraged. Nearly all of us in that part of the Marico had started farming again on what the government had given us. Now that the stock died we had nothing. First the drought had put us back to where we were when we started. Now with the miltsiek we couldn't hope to do anything. We couldn't even sow mealies, because, at the rate at which the cattle were dying, in a short while we would have no oxen left to pull the plough. People talked of selling what they had and going to look for work on the gold mines. We sent a petition to the government, but that did no good.

It was then that somebody got hold of the idea of trekking. In a few days we were talking of nothing else. But the question was where we could trek to. They would not allow us into Rhodesia for fear we might spread the miltsiek there as well. And it was useless going to any other part of the Transvaal. Somebody mentioned German West Africa. We had none of us been there before, and I suppose that really was the reason why, in the end, we decided to go there.

'The blight of the English is over South Africa,' Gerhardus Grobbelaar said. 'We'll remain here only to die. We must go away somewhere where there is not the Englishman's flag.'

In a few weeks' time we arranged everything. We were going to trek across the Kalahari into German territory. Everything we had we loaded up. We drove the cattle ahead and followed behind on our waggons. There were five families: the Steyns, the Grobbelaars, the Odendaals, the Ferreiras and Sannie and I. Webber also came with us. I think it was not so much that he was anxious to leave as that he and Koos Steyn had become very much attached to one another, and the Englishman did not wish to remain alone behind.

The youngest person in our trek was Koos Steyn's daughter Jemima, who was then about eighteen months old. Being the baby, she was a favourite with all of us.

Webber sold his waggon and went with Koos Steyn's trek.

When at the end of the first day we outspanned several miles inside the Bechuanaland Protectorate, we were very pleased that we were done with the Transvaal, where we had had so much misfortune. Of course, the Protectorate was also British territory, but all the same we felt happier there than we had done in our country. We saw Webber every day now, and although he was a foreigner with strange ways, and would remain an uitlander until he died, yet we disliked him less than before for being a rooinek.

It was on the first Sunday that we reached Malopolole. For the first part of our way the country remained Bushveld. There were the same kind of thorn-trees that grew in the Marico, except that they became fewer the deeper into the Kalahari that we went. Also, the ground became more and more sandy, until even before we came to Malopolole it was all desert. But scattered thornbushes remained all the way. That Sunday we held a religious service. Gerhardus Grobbelaar read a chapter out of the Bible and offered up a prayer. We sang a number of psalms, after which Gerhardus prayed again. I shall always remember that Sunday and the way we sat on the ground beside one of the waggons, listening to Gerhardus. That was the last Sunday that we were all together.

The Englishman sat next to Koos Steyn and the baby Jemima lay down in front of him. She played with Webber's fingers and tried to bite them. It was funny to watch her. Several times Webber looked down at her and smiled. I thought then that although Webber was not one of us, yet Jemima certainly did not know it. Maybe in a thing like that the child was wiser than we were. To her it made no difference that the man whose fingers she bit was born in another country and did not speak the same language that she did.

There are many things that I remember about that trek into the Kalahari. But one thing that now seems strange to me is the way in which, right from the first day, we took Gerhardus Grobbelaar for our leader. Whatever he said we just seemed to do without talking very much about it. We all felt that it was right simply because Gerhardus wished it. That was a strange thing about our trek. It was not simply that we knew Gerhardus had got the Lord with him – for we did know that – but it was rather that we believed in Gerhardus as well as in the Lord. I think that even if Gerhardus Grobbelaar had been an ungodly man we would still have followed him in exactly the same way. For when you are in the desert and there is no water and the way back is long, then you feel that it is better to have with you a strong man who does not read the Book very much, than a man who is good and religious, and yet does not seem sure how far to trek each day and where to outspan.

But Gerhardus Grobbelaar was a man of God. At the same time there was something about him that made you feel that it was only by acting as he advised that you could succeed. There was only one other man I have ever known who found it so easy to get people to do as he wanted. And that was Paul Kruger.

He was very much like Gerhardus Grobbelaar, except that Gerhardus was less quarrelsome. But of the two Paul Kruger was the bigger man.

Only once do I remember Gerhardus losing his temper. And that was with the Nagmaal at Elandsberg. It was on a Sunday, and we were camped out beside the Crocodile River. Gerhardus went round early in the morning from waggon to waggon and told us that he wanted everybody to come over to where his waggon stood. The Lord had been good to us at that time, so that we had had much rain and our cattle were fat. Gerhardus explained that he wanted to hold a service, to thank the Lord for all His good works, but more especially for what He had done for the farmers of the northern part of the Groot Marico District. This was a good plan, and we all came together with our Bibles and hymn-books. But one man, Karel Pieterse, remained behind at his waggon. Twice Gerhardus went to call him, but Karel Pieterse lay down on the grass and would not get up to come to the service. He said it was all right thanking the Lord now that there had been rains, but what about all those seasons when there had been drought and the cattle had died of thirst. Gerhardus Grobbelaar shook his head sadly, and said there was nothing he could do then, as it was Sunday. But he prayed that the Lord would soften Brother Pieterse's heart, and he finished off his prayer by saying that in any case, in the morning, he would help to soften the brother's heart himself.

The following morning Gerhardus walked over with a sjambok and an ox-riem to where Karel Pieterse sat before his fire, watching the kaffir making coffee. They were both of them men who were big in the body. But Gerhardus got the better of the struggle. In the end he won. He fastened Karel to the wheel of his own waggon with the ox-riem. Then he thrashed him with the sjambok while Karel's wife and children were looking on.

That had happened years before. But nobody had forgotten. And now, in the Kalahari, when Gerhardus summoned us to a service, it was noticed that no man stayed away.

Just outside Malopolole is a muddy stream that is dry part of the year and part of the year has a foot or so of brackish water.

We were lucky in being there just at the time when it had water. Early the following morning we filled up the water-barrels that we had put on our waggons before leaving the Marico. We were going right into the desert, and we did not know where we would get water again. Even the Bakwena kaffirs could not tell us for sure.

'The Great Dorstland Trek,' Koos Steyn shouted as we got ready to move off. 'Anyway, we won't fare as badly as the Dorstland Trekkers. We'll lose less cattle than they did because we've got less to lose. And seeing that we are only five families, not more than about a dozen of us will die of thirst.'

I thought it was bad luck for Koos Steyn to make jokes like that about the Dorstland Trek, and I think that others felt the same about it. We trekked right through that day, and it was all desert. By sunset we had not come across a sign of water anywhere. Abraham Ferreira said towards evening that perhaps it would be better if we went back to Malopolole and tried to find out for sure which was the best way of getting through the Kalahari. But the rest said that there was no need to do that, since we would be sure to come across water the next day. And, anyway, we were Doppers and, having once set out, we were not going to turn back. But after we had given the cattle water our barrels did not have too much left in them.

By the middle of the following day all our water had given out except a little that we kept for the children. But still we pushed on. Now that we had gone so far we were afraid to go back because of the long way that we would have to go without water to get back to Malopolole. In the evening we were very anxious. We all knelt down in the sand and prayed. Gerhardus Grobbelaar's voice sounded very deep and earnest when he besought God to have mercy on us, especially for the sakes of the little ones. He mentioned the baby Jemima by name. The Englishman knelt down beside me, and I noticed that he shivered when Gerhardus mentioned Koos Steyn's child.

It was moonlight. All around us was the desert. Our waggons seemed very small and lonely; there was something about them that looked very mournful. The women and the children put their arms round one another and wept a long while. Our kaffirs stood some distance away and watched us. My wife Sannie put her hand in mine, and I thought of the concentration camp. Poor woman, she had suffered much. And I knew that her thoughts were the same as my own: that after all it was perhaps better that our children should have died then than now.

We had got so far into the desert that we began telling one another that we must be near the end. Although we knew that German West was far away, and that in the way we had been travelling we had got little more than into the beginning of the Kalahari, yet we tried to tell one another lies about how near water was likely to be. But, of course, we told those lies only to one another. Each man in his own heart knew what the real truth was. And later on we even stopped telling one another lies about what a good chance we had of getting out alive. You can understand how badly things had gone with us when you know that we no longer troubled about hiding our position from the women and children. They wept, some of them. But that made no difference then. Nobody tried to comfort the women and children who cried. We knew that tears were useless, and yet somehow at that hour we felt that the weeping of the women was not less useless than the courage of the men. After a while there was no more weeping in our camp. Some of the women who lived through the dreadful things of the days that came after, and got safely back to the Transvaal, never again wept. What they had seen appeared to have hardened them. In this respect they had become as men. I think that is the saddest thing that ever happens in this world, when women pass through great suffering that makes them become as men.

That night we hardly slept. Early the next morning the men went out to look for water. An hour after sun-up Ferreira came back and told us that he had found a muddy pool a few miles away. We all went there, but there wasn't much water. Still, we got a little, and that made us feel better. It was only when it came to driving our cattle towards the mudhole that we found our kaffirs had deserted us during the night. After we had gone to sleep they had stolen away. Some of the weaker cattle couldn't get up to go to the pool. So we left them. Some were trampled to death or got choked in the mud, and we had to pull them out to let the rest get to the hole. It was pitiful.

Just before we left one of Ferreira's daughters died. We scooped a hole in the sand and buried her.

So we decided to trek back.

After his daughter was dead Abraham Ferreira went up to Gerhardus and told him that if we had taken his advice earlier on and gone back, his daughter would not have died.

'Your daughter is dead now, Abraham,' Gerhardus said. 'It is no use talking about her any longer. We all have to die some day. I refused to go back earlier. I have decided to go back now.'

Abraham Ferreira looked Gerhardus in the eyes and laughed. I shall always remember how that laughter sounded in the desert. In Abraham's voice there was the hoarseness of the sand and thirst. His voice was cracked with what the desert had done to him; his face was lined and his lips were blackened. But there was nothing about him that spoke of grief for his daughter's death.

'Your daughter is still alive, Oom Gerhardus,' Abraham Ferreira said, pointing to the waggon wherein lay Gerhardus' wife, who was weak, and the child to whom she had given birth only a few months before. 'Yes, she is still alive . . . so far.'

Ferreira turned away laughing, and we heard him a little later explaining to his wife in cracked tones about the joke he had made.

Gerhardus Grobbelaar merely watched the other man walk away without saying anything. So far we had followed Gerhardus through all things, and our faith in him had been great. But now that he had decided to trek back we lost our belief in him. We lost it suddenly, too. We knew that it was best to turn back, and that to continue would mean that we would all die in the Kalahari. And yet, if Gerhardus had said we must still go on we would have done so. We would have gone through with him right to the end. But now that he as much as said he was beaten by the desert we had no more faith in Gerhardus. That is why I have said that Paul Kruger was a greater man than Gerhardus. Because Paul Kruger was that kind of man whom we still worshipped even when he decided to retreat. If it had been Paul Kruger who told us that we had to go back we would have returned with strong hearts. We would have retained exactly the same love for our leader, even if we knew that he was beaten. But from the moment that Gerhardus said we must go back we all knew that he was no longer our leader. Gerhardus knew that also.

We knew what lay between us and Malopolole and there was grave doubt in our hearts when we turned our waggons round. Our cattle were very weak, and we had to inspan all that could walk. We hadn't enough yokes, and therefore we cut poles from the scattered bushes and tied them to the trek chains. As we were also without skeis we had to fasten the necks of the oxen straight on to the yokes with strops, and several of the oxen got strangled.

Then we saw that Koos Steyn had become mad. For he refused to return. He inspanned his oxen and got ready to trek on. His wife sat silent in the waggon with the baby; wherever her husband went she would go, too. That was only right, of course. Some women kissed her goodbye, and cried. But Koos Steyn's wife did not cry. We reasoned with Koos about it, but he said that he had made up his mind to cross the Kalahari, and he was not going to turn back just for nonsense.

'But, man,' Gerhardus Grobbelaar said to him, 'you've got no water to drink.'

'I'll drink coffee then,' Koos Steyn answered, laughing as always, and took up the whip and walked away beside the waggon. And Webber went off with him, just because Koos Steyn had been good to him, I suppose. That's why I have said that Englishmen are queer. Webber must have known that if Koos Steyn had not actually gone wrong in the head, still what he was doing now was madness, and yet he stayed with him.

We separated. Our waggons went slowly back to Malopolole. Koos Steyn's waggon went deeper into the desert. My waggon went last. I looked back at the Steyns. At that moment Webber also looked round. He saw me and waved his hand. It reminded me of that day in the Boer War when that other Englishman, whose companion we had shot, also turned round and waved.

Eventually we got back to Malopolole with two waggons and a

handful of cattle. We abandoned the other waggons. Awful things happened on that desert. A number of children died. Gerhardus Grobbelaar's waggon was in front of me. Once I saw a bundle being dropped through the side of the waggon-tent. I knew what it was. Gerhardus would not trouble to bury his dead child, and his wife lay in the tent too weak to move. So I got off the waggon and scraped a small heap of sand over the body. All I remember of the rest of the journey to Malopolole is the sun and the sand. And the thirst. Although at one time we thought that we had lost our way, yet that did not matter much to us. We were past feeling. We could neither pray nor curse, our parched tongues cleaving to the roofs of our mouths.

Until today I am not sure how many days we were on our way back, unless I sit down and work it all out, and then I suppose I get it wrong. We got back to Malopolole and water. We said we would never go away from there again. I don't think that even those parents who had lost children grieved about them then. They were stunned with what they had gone through. But I knew that later on it would all come back again. Then they would remember things about shallow graves in the sand, and Gerhardus Grobbelaar and his wife would think of a little bundle lying out in the Kalahari. And I knew how they would feel.

Afterwards we fitted out a waggon with fresh oxen; we took an abundant supply of water and went back into the desert to look for the Steyn family. With the help of the Sechuana kaffirs, who could see tracks that we could not see, we found the waggon. The oxen had been outspanned; a few lay dead beside the waggon. The kaffirs pointed out to us footprints on the sand, which showed which way those two men and that woman had gone.

In the end we found them.

Koos Steyn and his wife lay side by side in the sand; the woman's head rested on the man's shoulder; her long hair had become loosened, and blew softly in the wind. A great deal of fine sand had drifted over their bodies. Near them the Englishman lay, face downwards. We never found the baby Jemima. She must have died somewhere along the way and Koos Steyn must have buried her. But we agreed that the Englishman Webber must have passed through terrible things; he could not even have had any understanding left as to what the Steyns had done with their baby. He probably thought, up to the moment when he died, that he was carrying the child. For, when we lifted his body, we found, still clasped in his dead and rigid arms, a few old rags and a child's clothes.

It seemed to us that the wind that always stirs in the Kalahari blew very quietly and softly that morning.

Yes, the wind blew very gently.

Cometh Comet

Hans Engelbrecht was the first farmer in the Schweizer-Reneke district to trek (Oom Schalk Lourens said). With his wife and daughter and what was left of his cattle, he moved away to the northern slopes of the Dwarsberge, where the drought was less severe. Afterwards he was joined by other farmers from the same area. I can still remember how untidy the veld looked in those days, with rotting carcasses and sun-bleached bones lying about everywhere. Day after day we had stood at the boreholes, pumping an ever-decreasing trickle of brackish water into the cattle troughs. We watched in vain for a sign of a cloud. And it seemed that if anything did fall out of that sky, it wouldn't do us much good: it would be a shower of brimstone, most likely.

Still, it was a fine time for the aasvoëls and the crows. That was at the beginning, of course. Afterwards, when all the carcasses had been picked bare, and the Boers had trekked, most of the birds of prey flew away, also.

We trekked away in different directions. Four or five families eventually came to a halt at the foot of the Dwarsberge, near the place where Hans Engelbrecht was outspanned. In a vast area of the Schweizer-Reneke district only one man had chosen to stay behind. He was Ocker Gieljan, a young bywoner who had worked for Hans Engelbrecht since his boyhood. Ocker Gieljan spoke rarely, and then his words did not always seem to us to make sense.

Hans Engelbrecht was only partly surprised when, on the morning that the ox-waggon was loaded and the long line of oxen that were skin and bone started stumbling along the road to the north, Ocker Gieljan made it clear that he was not leaving the farm. The native voorloper had already gone to the head of the span and Hans Engelbrecht's wife and his eighteen-year-old daughter, Maria, were seated on the waggon, under the tent-sail, when Ocker Gieljan suddenly declared that he had decided to stay behind on the farm 'to look after things here'.

This was another instance of Ocker Gieljan's saying something that did not make sense. There could be nothing for him to look after, there, since in the whole district hardly even a lizard was left alive.

Hans Engelbrecht was in no mood to waste time in arguing with a daft bywoner. Accordingly, he got the kaffirs to unload half-a-sack of mealie-meal and a quantity of biltong in front of Ocker Gieljan's mud-walled room.

During the past few years it had not rained much in the Marico bushveld, either. But there was at least water in the Malopo, and the grazing was fair. Several months passed. Every day, from our camp by the Malopo, we studied the skies, which were of an intense blue. There was no longer that yellow tinge in the air that we had got used to in the Schweizer-Reneke district. But there was never a rain cloud.

The time came, also, when Hans Engelbrecht was brought to understand that the Lord had visited still more trouble on himself and his family. A little while before we had trekked away from our farms, a young insurance agent had left the district suddenly for Cape Town. That was a long distance to run away, especially when you think of how bad the roads were in those days. And in some strange fashion it seemed to me as though that young insurance agent was actually our leader. For he stood, after all, with his light hat and short jacket, at the head of our flight out of the Schweizer-Reneke area.

It became a commonplace, after a while, for Maria Engelbrecht to be seen seated in the grass beside her father's waggon, weeping. Few pitied her. She must have sat in the grass too often, with that insurance agent with the pointed, polished shoes, Lettie Grobler said to some of the women – forgetting that there had been no grass left in the Schweizer-Reneke veld at the time when Hans Engelbrecht's daughter was being courted.

It was easy for Maria to wipe the tears from her face, another woman said. Easier than to wipe away her shame, the woman meant.

Now and again, from some traveller who had passed through Schweizer-Reneke, we who had trekked out of that stricken region would hear a few useless things about it. We learnt nothing that we did not already know. Ocker Gieljan was still on the Engelbrecht farm, we heard. And the only other living creature in the whole district was a solitary crow. A passing traveller had seen Ocker Gieljan at the borehole. He was pumping water into a trough for the crow, the traveller said.

'When his mealie-meal gives out, Ocker will find his way here, right enough,' Hans Engelbrecht growled impatiently.

Then the night came when, from our encampment beside the Malopo, we first saw the comet, in the place above the Dwarsberge rante where the sun had gone down. We all began to wonder what that new star with the long tail meant. Would it bring rain? We didn't know. We could see, of course, that the star was an omen. Even an uneducated kaffir would know that. But we did not know what sort of omen it was.

If the bark of the maroelas turned black before the pol-gras was in seed, we would know that it would be a long winter. And if a wind sprang up suddenly in the evening, blowing away from the sunset, we would next morning send the cattle out later to graze. We knew many things about the veld and the sky and the seasons. But even the oldest Free State farmer among us didn't know what effect a comet had on a mealie-crop.

Hans Engelbrecht said that we should send for Rev. Losper, the missionary who ministered to the Bechuanas at Ramoutsa. But the rest of us ignored his suggestion.

During the following nights the comet became more clearly visible. A young policeman on patrol in those parts called on us one evening. When we spoke to him about the star, he said that he could do nothing about it, himself. It was a matter for the higher authorities, he said, laughing.

Nevertheless, he had made a few calculations, the policeman

explained, and he had sent a report to Pretoria. He estimated that the star was twenty-seven and a half miles in length, and that it was travelling faster than a railway train. He would not be surprised if the star reached Pretoria before his report got there. That would spoil his chances of promotion, he added.

We did not take much notice of the policeman's remarks, however. For one thing, he was young. And, for another, we did not have much respect for the police.

'If a policeman doesn't even know how to get on to the spoor of a couple of kaffir oxen that I smuggle across the Bechuanaland border,' Thys Bekker said, 'how does he expect to be able to follow the footprints of a star across the sky? That is big man's work.'

The appearance of the comet caused consternation among the Bechuanas in the village of Ramoutsa, where the mission station was. It did not take long for some of their stories about the star to reach our encampment on the other side of the Malopo. And although, at first, most of us professed to laugh at what we said were just ignorant kaffir superstitions, yet in the end we also began to share something of the Bechuanas' fears.

'Have you heard what the kaffirs say about the new star?' Arnoldus Grobler, husband of Lettie Grobler, asked of Thys Bekker. 'They say that it is a red beast with a fat belly like a very great chief, and it is going to come to eat up every blade of grass and every living thing.'

'In that case, I hope he lands in Schweizer-Reneke,' Thys Bekker said. 'If that red beast comes down on my farm, all that will happen is that in a short while there will be a whole lot more bones lying around to get white in the sun.'

Some of us felt that it was wrong of Thys Bekker to treat the matter so lightly. Moreover, this story only emanated from Ramoutsa, where there were a mission station and a post office. But a number of other stories, that were in every way much better, started soon afterwards to come out of the wilder parts of the bushveld, travelling on foot. It seemed that the further a tribe of kaffirs lived away from civilization, the more detailed and dependable was the information they had about the comet.

I know that I began to feel that Hans Engelbrecht had made the right suggestion in the first place, when he had said that we should send for the missionary. And I sensed that a number of others in our camp shared my feelings. But not one of us wanted to make this admission openly.

In the end it was Hans Engelbrecht himself who sent to Ramoutsa for Rev. Losper. By that time the comet was – each night in its rising – higher in the heavens, and it soon got round that the new star portended the end of the world. Lettie Grobler went so far as to declare that she had seen the good Lord Himself riding in the tail of the comet. What convinced us that she had, indeed, seen the Lord, was when she said that He had on a hat of the same shape as the predikant in Zwartruggens wore.

Lettie Grobler also said that the Lord was coming down to punish all of us for the sins of Maria Engelbrecht. This thought disturbed us greatly. We began to resent Maria's presence in our midst.

It was then that Hans Engelbrecht had sent for the missionary.

Meanwhile, Rev. Losper had his hands full with the Bechuanas at Ramoutsa, who seemed on the point of panicking in earnest. The latest story about the comet had just reached them, and because it had come from somewhere out of the deepest part of Africa, where the natives wore arrows tipped with leopard fangs, stuck through their nostrils, like moustaches, it was easily the most terrifying story of all. The story had come to the village, thumped out on the tom-toms.

The Bechuana chief at Ramoutsa – so Rev. Losper told us afterwards – fell into such a terror at the message brought by the speaking drums, that he thrust a handful of earth into his mouth, without thinking. He would have swallowed it, too, the missionary said, if one of his indunas hadn't restrained him in time, pointing out to the chief that perhaps the drum-men had got the message wrong. For, since the post office had come to Ramoutsa, the kaffirs whose work in the village it was to receive and send out messages on their tom-toms had got somewhat out of practice.

Consequently, because of the tumult at Ramoutsa, it happened that Ocker Gieljan arrived at the encampment before Rev. Losper got there.

Ocker Gieljan looked very tired and dusty on that afternoon when he walked up to Hans Engelbrecht's waggon. He took off his hat and, smiling somewhat vacantly, sat down without speaking in the shade of the veld-tent, inside which Maria Engelbrecht lay on a mattress. Neither Hans Engelbrecht nor his wife asked Ocker Gieljan any questions about his journey from the Schweizer-Reneke farm. They knew that he could have nothing to tell.

Shortly afterwards, Ocker Gieljan made a communication to Hans Engelbrecht, speaking diffidently. Thereupon Hans Engelbrecht went into the tent and spoke to his wife and daughter. A few minutes later he came out, looking pleased with himself.

'Sit down here on this riempies-stoel, Ocker,' Hans Engelbrecht said to his prospective son-in-law, 'and tell me how you came to leave the farm.'

'I got lonely,' Ocker Gieljan answered, thoughtfully. 'You see, the crow flew away. I was alone, after that. The crow was then already weak. He didn't fly straight, like crows do. His wings wobbled.'

When he told me about this, years later, Hans Engelbrecht said that something in Ocker Gieljan's tone brought him a sudden vision of the way his daughter, Maria, had also left the Schweizer-Reneke district. With broken wings.

I thought that Rev. Losper looked relieved to find, on his arrival at the camp, some time later, that all that was required of him, now, was the performance of a marriage ceremony.

On the next night but one, Maria Engelbrecht's child was born. All the adults in our little trekker community came in the night and the rain – which had been falling steadily for many hours – with gifts for Maria and her child.

And when I saw the star again, during a temporary break in the rain clouds, it seemed to me that it was not such a new star, at all: that it was, indeed, a mighty old star.

Ox-waggons on Trek

When I see the rain beating white on the thorn-trees, as it does now (Oom Schalk Lourens said), I remember another time when it rained. And there was a girl in an ox-waggon who dreamed. And in answer to her dreaming a lover came, galloping to her side from out of the veld. But he tarried only a short while, this lover who had come to her from the mist of the rain and the warmth of her dreams.

Yet when he had gone there was a slow look in her eyes that must have puzzled her lover very much, for it was a look of satisfaction, almost.

There had been rain all the way up from Sephton's Nek, that time. And the five ox-waggons on the road to the north rolled heavily through the mud. We had been to Zeerust for the Nagmaal church service, which we attended once a year.

You know what it is with these Nagmaals.

The Lord spreads these festivities over so many days that you have not only got time to go to church, but you also get a chance of going to the bioscope. Sometimes you even get a chance of going to the bar. But then you must go in the back way, through the dark passage next to the draper's shop.

Because Zeerust is a small place, and if you are seen going into the bar during Nagmaal people are liable to talk. I can still remember how surprised I was, one morning when I went into that dark passage next to the draper's shop and found the predikant there, wiping his mouth. The predikant looked at me and shook his head solemnly, and I felt very guilty.

I knew the predikant was a good man and that he was quite overpowered at the thought that a member of his church was going into the bar, during Nagmaal, to drink cheap Cape dop. That was why his knees trembled so much that, if it hadn't been for the wall, I am sure he would not have been able to stand.

So I went to the bioscope instead.

The house was very crowded. I couldn't follow much of the picture at the beginning, but afterwards a little boy who sat next to me and understood English explained to me what it was all about.

There was a young man who had the job of what he called taking people for a ride. Afterwards he got into trouble with the police. But he was a good-looking young man, and his sweetheart was very sorry for him when they took him into a small room and fastened him down on to a sort of chair.

I can't tell what they did that for. All I know is that I have been a Boer War prisoner at St Helena, and they never gave me a chair to sit on. Only a long wooden bench that I had to scrub once a week.

Anyway, I don't know what happened to the young man after that, because he was still sitting in that chair when the band started playing an English hymn about King George, and everybody stood up.

And a few days later five ox-waggons, full of people who had been to the Zeerust Nagmaal, were trekking along the road that led back to the Groot Marico. Inside the waggon-tents sat the women and children, listening to the rain pelting against the canvas. By the side of the oxen the drivers walked, cracking their long whips while the rain beat in their faces.

Overhead everything was black, except for the frequent flashes of lightning that tore across the sky.

After I had walked in this manner for some time, I began to get lonely. So I handed my whip to the kaffir voorloper and went on ahead to Adrian Brand's waggon. For some distance I walked in silence beside Adrian, who had his trousers rolled up to his knees, and had much trouble to brandish his whip and at the same time keep the rain out of his pipe.

'It's Minnie,' Adrian Brand said suddenly, referring to his nineteen-year-old daughter. 'There is one place in Zeerust that Minnie should not go to. And every Nagmaal, to my sorrow, I find she has been there. And it all goes to her head.'

'Oh, yes,' I answered. 'It always does.'

All the same, I was somewhat startled at Adrian's remarks. Minnie didn't strike me as the sort of girl who would go and spend her father's money drinking peach brandy in the bar. I started wondering if she had seen me in that draper's passage. Then Adrian went on talking and I felt more at ease.

'The place where they show those moving pictures,' he explained. 'Every time Minnie goes there, she comes back with ideas that are useless for a farmer's daughter. But this last time has made her quite impossible. For one thing, she says she won't marry Frans du Toit any more. She says Frans is too honest.'

'Well, that needn't be a difficulty, Adrian,' I said. 'You can teach Frans du Toit a few of the things you have done. That will make him dishonest enough. Like the way you put your own brand on those oxen that strayed into your kraal. Or the way you altered the figures on the compensation forms after the rinderpest. Or the way –'

Adrian looked at me with some disfavour.

'It isn't that,' he interrupted me, while I was still trying to call to mind a lot of other things that he was able to teach Frans du Toit, 'Minnie wants a mysterious sort of man. She wants a man who is dishonest, but who has got foreign manners and a good heart. She saw a man like that at the picture place she went to, and since then –'

We both looked round together.

Through the mist of the white rain a horseman came galloping up towards our waggons. He rode fast. Adrian Brand and I stood and watched him.

By this time our waggons were some distance behind the others.

The horseman came thundering along at full gallop until he was abreast of us. Then he pulled up sharply, jerking the horse on to his hind legs.

The stranger told us that his name was Koos Fichardt and that he was on his way to the Bechuanaland Protectorate. Adrian Brand and I introduced ourselves, and shortly afterwards Fichardt accepted our invitation to spend the night with us.

We outspanned a mile or so farther on, drawing the five

waggons up close together and getting what shelter we could by spreading bucksails.

Next morning there was no more rain.

But by that time Koos Fichardt had seen Adrian Brand's daughter Minnie. So he decided to stay with us longer.

We trekked on again, and from where I walked beside my oxen I could see Koos Fichardt and Minnie. They sat at the back of Adrian Brand's waggon, hatless, with their legs hanging down and the morning breeze blowing through their hair, and it was evident that Minnie was fascinated by the stranger. Also, he seemed to be very much interested in her.

You do get like that, when there is suddenly a bright morning after long rains, and a low wind stirs the wet grass, and you feel, for a little while, that you know the same things that the veld knows, and in your heart are whisperings.

Most of the time they sat holding hands, Fichardt talking a great deal and Minnie nodding her pretty head at intervals and encouraging him to continue. And they were all lies he told her, I suppose, as only a young man in love really can tell lies.

I remembered what Adrian told me about the ideas Minnie had got after she had been to the bioscope. And when I looked carefully at Fichardt I perceived that in many respects he was like that man I saw in the picture who was being fastened on to a chair.

Fichardt was tall and dark and well-dressed. He walked with a swagger. He had easy and engaging manners, and we all liked him.

But I noticed one or two peculiar things about Koos Fichardt. For instance, shortly after our waggons had entered a clump of tall camel-thorn trees, we heard horse-hooves galloping towards us. It turned out that the riders were a couple of farmers living in the neighbourhood. But as soon as he heard the hoof-beats, Koos Fichardt let go of Minnie's hand and crept under a bucksail.

It would be more correct to say that he dived under – he was so quick.

I said to myself that Fichardt's action might have no meaning, of course. After all, it is quite permissible for a man to feel that he would suddenly like to take a look at what is underneath the bucksail he is sitting on. Also, if he wants to, there is no harm in his spending quite a while on this task. And it is only natural, after he has had a bucksail on top of him, that he should come out with his hair rather ruffled, and that his face should be pale.

That night, when we outspanned next to the Groen River, it was very pleasant. We all gathered round the camp-fire and roasted meat and cooked crushed mealies. We sang songs and told ghost stories. And I wondered what Frans du Toit – the honest youth whom Minnie had discarded in Zeerust – would have thought if he could see Minnie Brand and Koos Fichardt, sitting unashamedly in each other's arms, for all the world to see their love, while the light of the camp-fire cast a rich glow over the thrill that was on their faces.

And although I knew how wonderful were the passing moments for those two, yet somehow, somehow, because I had seen so much of the world, I also felt sorry for them.

The next day we did not trek.

The Groen River was in flood from the heavy rains, and Oupa van Tonder, who had lived a long time in the Cape and was well versed in the ways of rivers, and knew how to swim, even, told us that it would not be safe to cross the drift for another twenty-four hours. Accordingly we decided to remain camped out where we were until next morning.

At first Koos Fichardt was much disturbed by this news, explaining how necessary it was for him to get into the Bechuanaland Protectorate by a certain day. After a while, however, he seemed to grow more reconciled to the necessity of waiting until the river had gone down.

But I noticed that he frequently gazed out over the veld in the direction from which we had come. He gazed out rather anxiously, I thought.

Some of the men went shooting. Others remained at their waggons, doing odd jobs to the yokes or the trek chains. Koos Fichardt made himself useful in various little ways, among other things, helping Minnie with the cooking. They laughed and romped a good deal.

Night came, and the occupants of the five waggons again gathered round the blazing fire. In some ways, that night was even grander than the one before. The songs we sang were more rousing. The stories we told seemed to have more power in them.

There was much excitement the following morning by the time the waggons were ready to go through the drift. And the excitement did not lie only in the bustle of inspanning the oxen.

For when we crossed the river it was without Koos Fichardt, and there was a slow look in Minnie's eyes.

The waggons creaked and splashed into the water, and we saw Koos Fichardt for the last time, sitting on his horse, with a horseman in uniform on each side of him. And when he took off his hat in farewell he had to use both hands, because of the cuffs that held his wrists together.

But always what I will remember is that slow look in Minnie's eyes. It was a kind of satisfaction, almost, at the thought that all the things that came to the girl she saw in the picture had now come to her, too.

In the Withaak's Shade

Leopards? (Oom Schalk Lourens said). Oh, yes, there are two varieties on this side of the Limpopo. The chief difference between them is that the one kind of leopard has got a few more spots on it than the other kind. But when you meet a leopard in the veld, unexpectedly, you seldom trouble to count his spots to find out what kind he belongs to. That is unnecessary. Because, whatever kind of leopard it is that you come across in this way, you only do one kind of running. And that is the fastest kind.

I remember the occasion that I came across a leopard unexpectedly, and to this day I couldn't tell you how many spots he had, even though I had all the time I needed for studying him. It happened about midday, when I was out on the far end of my farm, behind a koppie, looking for some strayed cattle. I thought the cattle might be there because it is shady under those withaak trees, and there is soft grass that is very pleasant to sit on. After I had looked for the cattle for about an hour in this manner, sitting up against a tree-trunk, it occurred to me that I could look for them just as well, or perhaps even better, if I lay down flat. For even a child knows that cattle aren't so small that you have got to get on to stilts and things to see them properly.

So I lay on my back, with my hat tilted over my face, and my legs crossed, and when I closed my eyes slightly the tip of my boot, sticking up into the air, looked just like the peak of Abjaterskop.

Overhead a lonely aasvoël wheeled, circling slowly round and round without flapping his wings, and I knew that not even a calf could pass in any part of the sky between the tip of my toe and that aasvoël without my observing it immediately. What was more, I could go on lying there under the withaak and looking for the cattle like that all day, if necessary. As you know, I am not the sort of farmer to loaf about the house when there is man's work to be done.

The more I screwed up my eyes and gazed at the toe of my boot, the more it looked like Abjaterskop. By and by it seemed that it actually was Abjaterskop, and I could see the stones on top of it, and the bush trying to grow up its sides, and in my ears there was a far-off, humming sound, like bees in an orchard on a still day. As I have said, it was very pleasant.

Then a strange thing happened. It was as though a huge cloud, shaped like an animal's head and with spots on it, had settled on top of Abjaterskop. It seemed so funny that I wanted to laugh. But I didn't. Instead, I opened my eyes a little more and I felt glad to think that I was only dreaming. Because otherwise I would have to believe that the spotted cloud on Abjaterskop was actually a leopard, and that he was gazing at my boot. Again I wanted to laugh. But then, suddenly, I knew.

And I didn't feel so glad. For it was a leopard, all right – a large-sized, hungry-looking leopard, and he was sniffing suspiciously at my feet. I was uncomfortable. I knew that nothing I could do would ever convince that leopard that my toe was Abjaterskop. He was not that sort of leopard: I knew that without even counting the number of his spots. Instead, having finished with my feet, he started sniffing higher up. It was the most terrifying moment of my life. I wanted to get up and run for it. But I couldn't. My legs wouldn't work.

Every big-game hunter I have come across has told me the same story about how, at one time or another, he has owed his escape from lions and other wild animals to his cunning in lying down and pretending to be dead, so that the beast of prey loses interest in him and walks off. Now, as I lay there on the grass, with the leopard trying to make up his mind about me, I understood why, in such a situation, the hunter doesn't move. It's simply that he can't move. That's all. It's not his cunning that keeps him down. It's his legs.

In the meantime, the leopard had got up as far as my knees. He was studying my trousers very carefully, and I started getting embarrassed. My trousers were old and rather unfashionable.

Also, at the knee, there was a torn place, from where I had climbed through a barbed-wire fence, into the thick bush, the time I saw the government tax-collector coming over the bult before he saw me. The leopard stared at that rent in my trousers for quite a while, and my embarrassment grew. I felt I wanted to explain about the government tax-collector and the barbed wire. I didn't want the leopard to get the impression that Schalk Lourens was the sort of man who didn't care about his personal appearance.

When the leopard got as far as my shirt, however, I felt better. It was a good blue flannel shirt that I had bought only a few weeks ago from the Indian store at Ramoutsa, and I didn't care how many strange leopards saw it. Nevertheless, I made up my mind that next time I went to lie on the grass under the withaak, looking for strayed cattle, I would first polish up my veldskoens with sheep's fat, and I would put on my black hat that I only wear to Nagmaal. I could not permit the wild animals of the neighbourhood to sneer at me.

But when the leopard reached my face I got frightened again. I knew he couldn't take exception to my shirt. But I wasn't so sure about my face. Those were terrible moments. I lay very still, afraid to open my eyes and afraid to breathe. Sniff-sniff, the huge creature went, and his breath swept over my face in hot gasps. You hear of many frightening experiences that a man has in a lifetime. I have also been in quite a few perilous situations. But if you want something to make you suddenly old and to turn your hair white in a few moments, there is nothing to beat a leopard – especially when he is standing over you, with his jaws at your throat, trying to find a good place to bite.

The leopard gave a deep growl, stepped right over my body, knocking off my hat, and growled again. I opened my eyes and saw the animal moving away clumsily. But my relief didn't last long. The leopard didn't move far. Instead, he turned over and lay down next to me.

Yes, there on the grass, in the shade of the withaak, the leopard and I lay down together. The leopard lay half-curled up, on his side, with his forelegs crossed, like a dog, and whenever I tried to move away he grunted. I am sure that in the whole history of the Groot Marico there have never been two stranger companions engaged in the thankless task of looking for strayed cattle.

Next day, in Fanie Snyman's voorkamer, which was used as a post office, I told my story to the farmers of the neighbourhood, while they were drinking coffee and waiting for the motor-lorry from Zeerust.

'And how did you get away from that leopard in the end?' Koos van Tonder asked, trying to be funny. 'I suppose you crawled through the grass and frightened the leopard off by pretending to be a python.'

'No, I just got up and walked home,' I said. 'I remembered that the cattle I was looking for might have gone the other way and strayed into your kraal. I thought they would be safer with the leopard.'

'Did the leopard tell you what he thought of General Pienaar's last speech in the Volksraad?' Frans Welman asked, and they all laughed.

I told my story over several times before the lorry came with our letters, and although the dozen odd men present didn't say much while I was talking, I could see that they listened to me in the same way that they listened when Krisjan Lemmer talked. And everybody knew that Krisjan Lemmer was the biggest liar in the Bushveld.

To make matters worse, Krisjan Lemmer was there, too, and when I got to the part of my story where the leopard lay down beside me, Krisjan Lemmer winked at me. You know that kind of wink. It was to let me know that there was now a new understanding between us, and that we could speak in future as one Marico liar to another.

I didn't like that.

'Kêrels,' I said in the end, 'I know just what you are thinking. You don't believe me, and you don't want to say so.'

'But we do believe you,' Krisjan Lemmer interrupted me, 'very wonderful things happen in the Bushveld. I once had a twenty-foot mamba that I named Hans. This snake was so attached to me that I couldn't go anywhere without him. He would even follow me to church on a Sunday, and because he didn't care much for some of the sermons, he would wait for me outside under a tree. Not that Hans was irreligious. But he had a sensitive nature, and the strong line that the predikant took against the serpent in the Garden of Eden always made Hans feel awkward. Yet he didn't go and look for a withaak to lie under, like your leopard. He wasn't stand-offish in that way. An ordinary thorn-tree's shade was good enough for Hans. He knew he was only a mamba, and didn't try to give himself airs.'

I didn't take any notice of Krisjan Lemmer's stupid lies, but the upshot of this whole affair was that I also began to have doubts about the existence of that leopard. I recalled queer stories I had heard of human beings that could turn themselves into animals, and although I am not a superstitious man I could not shake off the feeling that it was a spook thing that had happened. But when, a few days later, a huge leopard had been seen from the roadside near the poort, and then again by Mtosas on the way to Nietverdiend, and again in the turf-lands near the Malopo, matters took a different turn.

At first people jested about this leopard. They said it wasn't a real leopard, but a spotted animal that had walked away out of Schalk Lourens' dream. They also said that the leopard had come to the Dwarsberge to have a look at Krisjan Lemmer's twenty-foot mamba. But afterwards, when they had found his spoor at several water-holes, they had no more doubt about the leopard.

It was dangerous to walk about in the veld, they said. Exciting times followed. There was a great deal of shooting at the leopard and a great deal of running away from him. The amount of Martini and Mauser fire I heard in the krantzes reminded me of nothing so much as the First Boer War. And the amount of running away reminded me of nothing so much as the Second Boer War.

But always the leopard escaped unharmed. Somehow, I felt sorry for him. The way he had first sniffed at me and then lain down beside me that day under the withaak was a strange thing that I couldn't understand. I thought of the Bible, where it is written that the lion shall lie down with the lamb.

But I also wondered if I hadn't dreamt it all. The manner in which those things had befallen me was all so unearthly. The leopard began to take up a lot of my thoughts. And there was no man to whom I could talk about it who would be able to help me in any way. Even now, as I am telling you this story, I am expecting you to wink at me, like Krisjan Lemmer did.

Still, I can only tell you the things that happened as I saw them, and what the rest was about only Africa knows.

It was some time before I again walked along the path that leads through the bush to where the withaaks are. But I didn't lie down on the grass again. Because when I reached the place, I found that the leopard had got there before me. He was lying on the same spot, half-curled up in the withaak's shade, and his forepaws were folded, as a dog's are, sometimes. But he lay very still. And even from the distance where I stood I could see the red splash on his breast where a Mauser bullet had gone.

A Boer Rip van Winkel

Every writer has got, lying around somewhere in a suitcase or a trunk, various parts of a story that he has worked on from time to time and that he has never finished, because he hasn't been able to find out how the theme should be handled. Such a story – that I have had lying in a suitcase for many years – centres around the things that happened to Herklaas van Wyk.

The plot of a story has no particular appeal for me. I feel that to sit down and work out a plot does not call for the highest form of literary inspiration. Rather does that form of activity recall the skill of the inventor.

My own stories that I like best are those that have just grown. Some mood, conjured up in half-a-dozen words, has set me going, and it has often happened to me that only when I have got to very near the end in the writing of it, has the shape of the story suddenly dawned on me. And more than once I have been surprised to find what a very old tale it was that had kept me from the chimney-corner. Agreeably surprised, that is, for I have a preference for old tales.

But my inability to finish writing the story of Herklaas van Wyk is not due to the denouement not having taken some recognizable form in my mind within the last few hundred words. It hasn't been that kind of a writer's problem: I didn't put my hand in the hat and a story came out that wouldn't unfold. On the contrary, this story told itself quite all right, in all its main essentials. What is more, within the first few paragraphs I realized very clearly to what general class of story it belonged. But there were so many hiatuses between the time when Herklaas van Wyk was last seen with the remnants of the Losberg commando, towards the end of the Boer War, in 1902, and the time when he was captured with General Kemp outside Upington in the rebellion of 1914.

If I could fill in that interval of a dozen years satisfactorily, I would still be able to write the story of Herklaas van Wyk. Yet the very fascination of this story is intimately bound up with the *nature* of that lacuna. It is no new thing to have a story of which the end is a mystery – something that the reader must work out for himself with or without a clue supplied by the author. But when the middle part of a story – which gives the atmosphere to the whole sequence of real and imaginary events – is missing, then I feel that I am confronted with an artistic problem of an order that I am not sure it is wise for a writer to tackle.

I don't mind writing a story in which the plot is vague. But when the atmosphere isn't there – the background and the psychology and the interplay of situation and character – then what is left isn't my idea of a story.

The events with which Herklaas van Wyk was connected in the early part of 1902 were commonplace enough. There are still a number of Boers alive today who were on commando with him. Kritzinger's invasion of the Cape Colony is an episode that has passed into history. And a considerable body of Boers, members of commandos that kept being split up into ever-smaller groups, succeeded in penetrating to the Atlantic Ocean and in remaining in the field, deep inside the Cape Colony, long after the main commando had retreated beyond the Vaal.

It was in 1902 that Herklaas van Wyk, then promoted to the rank of veld-kornet, caught sight, in the blue distance, of the unquiet Atlantic. The small body of men pushed on to the beach. They had come a long way, from the Transvaal and the Free State, and also from the Karoo, where a number of Cape rebels had joined the fighting forces of the Republics. It was a mixed group of burghers that came to a halt on the white sand of the beach south of Okiep.

Herklaas van Wyk rode his horse along the shore for a considerable distance. The burghers galloped on behind their veld-kornet, the hooves of their horses kicking up a spray of damp sea-sand. For they rode along that strip of beach from which the waves had withdrawn in the ebbing of the Atlantic.

Eventually Herklaas van Wyk reined in his horse. His hand

shielding his eyes, he gazed for a long while at the place where sea and sky met on the horizon. He had known two years before that the Boer War was lost for the Transvaal and the Free State. One last hope had returned to him, early that morning, when he had caught sight of the ocean. That hope, too, had vanished now. He realized that he would not be able, with the handful of burghers under his command, to invade England.

Facing out to the sea, Herklaas van Wyk slowly took off his hat.

'It's no good, kêrels,' he called out above the roar of the waves and the wind, 'we'll have to get back again. There's no drift around here where we'll be able to get our horses through.'

About Herklaas van Wyk there was a certain measure of grandeur even in defeat.

And his story, up to that time when the sea-wind was whistling through his black beard, was straightforward enough. In fact, you can read about him in any history book dealing with that period. But it is on his way back to the Transvaal, when he and his men had to elude flying English columns and had to cross barbed-wire fences with block-houses threaded on to them, that Herklaas van Wyk quits the pages of printed history, complete with dates and place names, and enters the realm of legend.

It is generally accepted that he was still in the field when the Boer War ended in May, 1902. His own story is that he crept into a deserted rondavel at the foot of a koppie in the Upington district, and that he fell asleep there, with his Mauser beside him, and his horse tethered to a thorn-tree.

Another story – subscribed to on doubtful authority by fellow members of the rebel commando that surrendered with Herklaas van Wyk in 1915, after General Kemp had failed to take Upington – seeks to account for that interval of a dozen years in a different fashion. In terms of this latter attempt at reconstructing the facts, all that happened to Herklaas van Wyk between 1902, the end of the Boer War, and 1914, the year of the outbreak of the rebellion, was that he lived on some farm in the Upington district as a bywoner. It is readily conceivable, protagonists of this standpoint declare, that he slept quite a lot during that period, especially on hot afternoons when his employer had sent him out to look for strayed cattle. Who has not heard – this school of the doubters asks – of a bywoner lying asleep in his rondavel when he should be at the borehole pumping water?

I can only reply that this theory which represents him as a decadent bywoner does not fit in with my conception of Herklaas van Wyk as a person.

A third school of theorists, drawing attention to the scar of an old bullet-wound that Herklaas van Wyk still carried above his left temple when he rode with Kemp in 1915, offers another explanation of that interim period. Quite likely that bullet, searing the flesh at the side of his head, caused loss of memory, they say. Quite likely Herklaas van Wyk did become a bywoner when the Boer War ended. And then, in 1914, when he again heard the hoof-beats of commandos coming out of the veld, and the rattling of musketry, the past was suddenly brought back to him, and he was once more in the saddle, with his Mauser and bandolier. The Boer War came back to him in a single rush. Only, the bywoner period now sank into oblivion. Memory does play tricks like that.

Well, I must confess that I don't care particularly for this latter theory, either.

I still prefer Herklaas van Wyk's own story, which he told to anybody who would listen, after he had been captured by Botha's government forces. For one thing, if we accept Herklaas van Wyk's account of his long sleep in the abandoned rondavel at the foot of a koppie in the Upington district, we have the material for a South African legend as stirring as the one that Washington Irving chronicled. Van Wyk and Van Winkel. This is surely no idle coincidence. Above all, there is a Gothic quality in Herklaas van Wyk's own story – a gloomy magnificence that is never absent from the interior of a rondavel at the foot of a koppie, if that koppie is composed of ironstone.

Herklaas van Wyk asleep in a dark corner, waiting, a backveld Barbarossa, for his far-off awakening, in an hour filled with the thunder of horse-hooves and the noise of battle.

*

The old man with the white beard and the rusty Mauser and the walking skeleton of a horse had been with Kemp's rebel commando for the best part of a week of dispirited running away from the government forces. It now began to dawn on the little band of 1914 rebels that Oom Herklaas van Wyk was (as they interpreted it) in his second childhood. It was clear that he thought that the year was still 1902; it was obvious that he did not know that he was a rebel who had taken the field against the Union troops; instead, he spoke of himself as a Transvaal burgher, and he referred to Cronjé's surrender at Paardeberg, scornfully, as though it had taken place yesterday.

He was very puzzled, also, when he learnt for the first time that the rebel commando was being pursued by a column of Botha-men.

'But if Botha is chasing us,' Herklaas van Wyk demanded, 'who is fighting Kitchener?'

Thus it came about, one evening when the rebels were encamped in a bluegum plantation on the road to Upington, that a lot of explanations were made.

'I remember the day you joined us, Oom Herklaas,' Jan Gouws, a young rebel, said, after Herklaas van Wyk had told his story, and they had persuaded him that the year was, indeed, 1915, and that he was not now fighting in the Boer War. 'Your white beard was blowing in the wind, Oom Herklaas, and several of us laughed at the awkward way your old horse cantered, throwing his legs all to one side. So you really say you slept for twelve years?'

'I believe now – now that you've told me,' Herklaas van Wyk replied, 'that I must have lain asleep on the floor of that rondavel all those years. That must have been just at the end of the Boer War. And it's funny that I didn't wake up before my nation again needed me.'

The rebels received the old man's last remark in silence. They were beginning to doubt the wisdom of their armed rising. They had been driven from pillar to post for many days. Incessant rain had damped their ardour.

'Did you remember to wind your watch before you went to sleep in that rondavel, Oom Herklaas?' Jan Gouws asked, trying to change the subject.

The others did not laugh at this sally. For one thing, the rain had started coming down again . . .

Some of the rebels seemed half-inclined to believe Herklaas van Wyk's story. And there seemed to be something inexplicably solemn in the thought of a burgher of the Transvaal Republic going to sleep in the corner of a deserted rondavel, with his Mauser at his side – and only waking up again a dozen years later, when men were once more riding with rifles slung across their shoulders.

'Did you dream at all during that time, Oom Herklaas?' another man asked, in a half-serious tone.

The old man thought for a little while.

'I remember dreaming about a mossie settling on a kaffirboom that was full of red flowers,' Herklaas van Wyk answered slowly, 'but I think I dreamt of it a long time back – after I had been asleep only four years, or so.'

Jan Gouws shivered. The red flowers on that kaffirboom must be pretty well faded by now, he thought. And it gave him a queer feeling to think of that mossie . . . that an old man saw in a dream . . . flitting about in the sunshine of long ago. It made Jan Gouws feel uncomfortable, for a reason that he could not explain.

'My Mauser is very rusty,' Herklaas van Wyk continued. 'I've tried oiling it, but that doesn't help. I'll have to hands-up or shoot one of the enemy, and take his Lee-Metford off him, like we used to do. How long will it take us to win this war, do you think?'

The rebels did not answer. They knew that their cause was already shot to pieces. In spite of the old man's senility, there seemed to emanate from his spirit a strange kind of assurance, a form of steadfastness in the face of adversity and defeat that they themselves did not possess. It seemed that there was something inside the entrails of this burgher of the Transvaal Republic that they didn't have. Something firm and constant that they had lost. And they felt, sensing the difference between the previous generation and their own, and without being able to express their feelings in words, that in that difference lay their defeat.

'What happened about your horse, Oom Herklaas?' a young rebel asked eventually.

Exteriorly dilapidated, Herklaas van Wyk still seemed to represent, somehow, the gloom and the grandeur of a great day.

'I had tethered my horse to a thorn-tree,' Herklaas van Wyk said, 'and he, too, must have fallen asleep. And I am sure that the hoof-beats of a commando at full gallop must have awakened him, also. For when I got to the thorn-tree – which hadn't grown much during that time: you know how slowly a thorn-tree grows – my old war-horse was sniffing the wind and pawing the ground. And his neck was arched.'

In Church

Inside the schoolroom at Droogtebult there was the smell of cheap scent and stale powder mixed with sweat. The room was crowded on that Sunday morning, for a church service between the quarterly Nagmaals was an unusual event. There were present members of both Dutch churches, the Hervormde and the Gereformeerde, and the minister gave out only psalms, as he did not wish to antagonize the Doppers, who do not sing hymns.

Gerhardina Brink sat at the end of a row of school-benches. In that same row were her father and mother and her younger brothers and sisters. Gerhardina was the eldest of Thys Brink's children. She was sixteen. But already there was a fullness about her breasts and a maturity of development about her hips that elsewhere would be associated with a woman much older than Gerhardina. The Bushveld sun, ripening the kaffircorn and the mealies, also ripened the women very early, perhaps even before their time. Already there had been young men who had courted Thys Brink's daughter. There was the new school-teacher, for instance, who had come often to the farm and had sat up with Gerhardina. But lately he had stayed away. It was rumoured that he had applied to the Education Department for a transfer to a school on the Highveld. They said that the Bushveld climate did not agree with him.

While they were singing 'Prys den Heer', Gerhardina looked up from the book and encountered the gaze of the school-teacher. She had tried often during the service to catch his eye, but always he had seemed to look past her. But now there was no doubt about it. She had looked at him at the same time that he had looked at her. Yes, he had seen her, right enough . . . and all he did was to turn his head away quickly and stare at something on the wall. Suddenly Gerhardina felt a sickness within her. She heard her father's voice droning the words of the psalm through his beard. She saw Lena van Heerden glance at her strangely and she blushed. She watched the minister putting slips of paper in his Bible for place-marks. And all the time within her was that terribly sick feeling.

She was relieved when the singing was over and she could sit down again.

The minister was a young man who had only recently qualified at the Potchefstroom Theological Seminary. He was obviously nervous. He cleared his throat frequently and stuttered even in reading the text. But the people to whom he preached had a respect for all ministers. It was a reverence that stretched back for many generations. It was older than the Transvaal Republic. It was older than the Great Trek. It was older than Van Riebeeck. So now though the minister stuttered and was nervous, the congregation did not notice it.

'Sing, O barren, thou that didst not bear,' he read. 'Break forth into singing and cry aloud, thou that didst not travail with child.'

Gerhardina listened to these words. Somehow, she felt that she understood what those words meant, in a way that the minister could not understand them. She felt that it was just as though she had all at once become an old woman. The minister went on to talk about Isaiah, but she did not hear him. Again she glanced hurriedly at the school-teacher, but he must have expected something like that, because his face was still turned away from her, and he was still studying that same part of the wall. The minister kept talking, his nervousness beginning to wear off. Near the back a baby in arms started crying. It was a thin, pitiful sort of wail, and everybody turned round, as though they had never before heard a child cry. The mother rocked the baby to and fro in an effort to soothe it, but without success; she then walked out and stood in the sun in front of the door and nuzzled the child at her breast. A number of men near the door turned round and watched the operation idly.

'Thou that didst not travail with child,' Gerhardina murmured to herself. She wondered if Lena van Heerden really had looked at her in a peculiar way, or if she had only imagined it. But there was no imagination about the way in which the teacher had purposely tried to avoid her.

Then she looked at her father and mother. She wondered how many times she had seen her father sit just that way in church, his shoulders hunched forward, his eyes half-closed, his black coat – which with age was becoming green in places – sprinkled at the collar with dandruff. Her mother had a handkerchief up to her eyes. There never yet had been a sermon preached that did not move her mother.

Gerhardina was pleased when the last psalm had been sung and the minister had pronounced the blessing. She walked on alone to the mule-cart which was standing under a thorn-tree. Her parents remained around the school building for a while, talking to different people. Also, her father was anxious to get in a word with the minister, because if people saw him conversing with the minister in an intimate kind of way it would help his chances of getting nominated as ouderling. Her brothers and sisters stayed with their parents, but Gerhardina wanted to be alone.

'I saw that school-teacher,' her father said when they got into the cart. 'He was talking to Frikkie Haasbroek. When I came along he slunk away like a dog that steals fat. He doesn't come to see you any more, either. If he thinks we're not good enough for him, he can . . .'

So her father went on.

Why couldn't people understand? Gerhardina wondered. Still, they would know one of these days. She couldn't go on concealing it much longer. Already, it seemed that Lena van Heerden looked at her as if she knew. Yet it didn't matter. There was always a way out.

But on the road back to the farm Gerhardina admitted to herself that, when the time came, she would lack the courage to drink sheep-dip, like Sophie Lombard had done when she was with child.

Secret Agent

The stranger who arrived on the government lorry from Bekkersdal told us that his name was Losper. He was having a look round that part of the Marico, he said, and he did not expect to stay more than a few days. He was dressed in city clothes and carried a leather briefcase. But because he did not wear pointed black shoes and did not say how sad it was that Flip Prinsloo should have died so suddenly at the age of sixty-eight, of snakebite, we knew that he was not a life insurance agent. Furthermore, because he did not once seek to steer the conversation round to the sinful practices of some people who offered a man a quite substantial bribe when he was just carrying out his duty, we also knew that the stranger was not a plainclothes man who had been sent round to investigate the increase in cattle-smuggling over the Conventie-lyn. Quite a number of us breathed more easily, then.

Nevertheless, we were naturally intrigued to know what Meneer Losper had come there for. But with the exception of Gysbert van Tonder – who did not have much manners since the time he had accompanied a couple of Americans on safari to the lower reaches of the Limpopo – we were all too polite to ask a man straight out what his business was, and then explain to him how he could do it better.

That trip with the two Americans influenced Gysbert van Tonder's mind, all right. For he came back talking very loudly. And he bought a waistcoat at the Indian store especially so that he could carry a cigar in it. And he spoke of himself as Gysbert O. van Tonder. And he once also slapped Dominee Welthagen on the back to express his appreciation of the Nagmaal sermon Dominee Welthagen had delivered on the Holy Patriarchs and the Prophets.

When Gysbert van Tonder came back from that journey, we understood how right the Voortrekker, Hendrik Potgieter, had been over a hundred years ago, when he said that the parts around the lower end of the Limpopo were no fit place for a white man.

We asked Gysbert van Tonder how that part of the country affected the two Americans. And he said he did not think it affected them *much*. But it was a queer sort of area, all round, Gysbert explained. And there was a lot of that back-slapping business, too. He said he could still remember how one of the Americans slapped Chief Umfutusu on the back and how Chief Umfutusu, in his turn, slapped the American on the ear with a clay-pot full of greenish drink that the chief was holding in his hand at the time.

The American was very pleased about it, Gysbert van Tonder said, and he devoted a lot of space to it in his diary. The American classed Chief Umfutusu's action as among the less understood tribal customs that had to do with welcoming distinguished White travellers. Later on, when Gysbert van Tonder and the Americans came to a Mshangaan village that was having some trouble with hut tax, the American who kept the diary was able to write a lot more about what he called an obscure African ritual that that tribe observed in welcoming a superior order of stranger. For that whole Mshangaan village, men, women and children, had rushed out and pelted Gysbert and the two Americans with wet cow-dung.

In his diary the American compared this incident with the ceremonial greeting that a tribe of Bavendas once accorded the explorer Stanley, when they threw him backwards into a dam – to show respect, as Stanley explained, afterwards.

Well anyway, here was this stranger, Losper, a middle-aged man with a suitcase, sitting in the post office and asking Jurie Steyn if he could put him up in a spare room for a few days, while he had a look round.

'I'll pay the same rates as I paid in the boarding-house in Zeerust,' Meneer Losper said. 'Not that I think you might overcharge me, of course, but I am only allowed a fixed sum by the department for accommodation and travelling expenses.'

'Look here, Neef Losper –' Jurie Steyn said. 'You didn't tell me your first name, so I can only call you Neef Losper –'

'My first name is Org,' the stranger said.

'Well, then, Neef Org,' Jurie Steyn went on. 'From the way you talk I can see that you are unacquainted with the customs of the Groot Marico. In the first place, I am a postmaster and a farmer. I don't know which is the worst job, what with money orders and the blue-tongue. I have got to put axle grease on my mule-cart and sealing wax on the mailbag. And sometimes I get mixed up. Any man in my position would. One day I'll paste a revenue stamp on my off-mule and I'll brand a half-moon and a bar on the Bekkersdal mailbag. Then there will be trouble. There will be trouble with my off-mule, I mean. The post office won't notice any difference. But my off-mule is funny, that way. He'll pull the mule-cart, all right. But then everything has got to be the way *he* wants it. He won't have people laughing at him because he's got a revenue stamp stuck on his behind. I sometimes think that my off-mule *knows* that a shilling revenue stamp is what you put on a piece of paper after you've told a Justice of the Peace a lot of lies –'

'Not lies,' Gysbert van Tonder interjected.

'A lot of lies,' Jurie Steyn went on, 'about another man's cattle straying into a person's lucerne lands while that person was taking his sick child to Zeerust –'

Gysbert van Tonder, who was Jurie Steyn's neighbour, half-rose out of his riempies-chair, then, and made some sneering remarks about Jurie Steyn and his off-mule. He said he never had much time for either of them. And he said he would not like to describe the way his lucerne lands looked after Jurie Steyn's cattle had finished straying over them. He said he would not like to use that expression, because there was a stranger present.

Meneer Losper seemed interested, then, and sat well forward to listen. And it looked as though Gysbert van Tonder would have said the words, too. Only, At Naudé, who has a wireless to which he listens in regularly, put a stop to the argument. He said that this was a respectable voorkamer, with family portraits on the wall.

'And there's Jurie Steyn's wife in the kitchen, too,' At Naudé said. 'You can't use the same sort of language here as in the Volksraad, where there are all men.'

Actually, Jurie Steyn's wife had gone out of the kitchen, about then. Ever since that young schoolmaster with the black hair parted in the middle had come to Bekkersdal, Jurie Steyn's wife had taken a good deal of interest in education matters. Consequently, when the stranger, Org Losper, said he was from the department, Jurie Steyn's wife thought right away – judging from his shifty appearance – that he might be a school inspector. And so sent a message to the young schoolmaster to warn him in time, so that he could put away the saws and hammers that he used for the private fretwork that he did in front of the class while the children were writing compositions.

In the meantime, Jurie Steyn was getting to the point.

'So you can't expect me to be running a boarding-house as well as everything else, Neef Org,' he was saying. 'But all the same, you are welcome to stay. And you can stay as long as you like. Only, you must not offer again to pay. If you had known more about these parts, you would also have known that the Groot Marico has got a very fine reputation for hospitality. When you come and stay with a man he gets insulted if you offer him money. But I shall be glad to invite you into my home as a member of my own family.'

Then Org Losper said that that was exactly what he didn't want, any more. And he was firm about it, too.

'When you're a member of the family, you can't say no to anything,' he explained. 'In the Pilanesberg I tore my best trousers on the wire. I was helping, as a member of the family, to round up the donkeys for the water-cart. At Nietverdiend a Large White bit a piece out of my second best trousers and my leg. That was when I was a member of the family and was helping to carry buckets of swill to the pig troughs. The farmer said the Large White was just being playful that day. Well, maybe the Large

White thought I was also a member of the family – *his* family, I mean. At Abjaterskop I nearly fell into a disused mine shaft on a farm there. Then I was a member of the family, assisting to throw a dead bull down the shaft. The bull had died of anthrax and I was helping to pull him by one haunch and I was walking backwards and when I jumped away from the opening of the mine shaft it was almost too late.

'I can also tell you what happened to me in the Dwarsberge when I was also a member of the family. And also about what happened when I was a member of the family at Derdepoort. I did not know that that family was having a misunderstanding with the family next door about water rights. And it was when I was opening a water furrow with a shovel that a load of No. A buckshot went through my hat. As a member of the family, I was standing ankle-deep in the mud at the time, and so I couldn't run very fast. So you see, when I say I would rather pay, it is not that I am ignorant of the very fine tradition that the Marico has for the friendly and bountiful entertainment that it accords the stranger. But I do not wish to presume further on your kindness. If I have much more bushveld hospitality I might never see my wife and children again. It's all very well being a member of somebody else's family. But I have a duty to my *own* family. I want to get back to them alive.'

Johnny Coen remarked that next time Gysbert van Tonder had an American tourist on his hands, he need not take him to the Limpopo, but could just show him around the Marico farms.

It was then that Gysbert van Tonder asked Org Losper straight out what his business was. And, to our surprise, the stranger was very frank about it.

'It is a new job that has been made for me by the Department of Defence,' Org Losper said. 'There wasn't that post before. You see, I worked very hard at the last elections, getting people's names taken off the electoral roll. You have no idea how many names I got taken off. I even got some of our candidate's supporters crossed off. But you know how it is, we all make mistakes. It is a very secret post. It is a top Defence secret. I am under oath not to disclose anything about it. But I am free to tell you that I am making certain investigations on behalf of the Department of Defence. I am trying to find out *whether something has been seen here*. But, of course, the post has been made for me, if you understand what I mean.'

We said we understood, all right. And we also knew that, since he was under oath about it, the nature of Org Losper's investigations in the Groot Marico would leak out sooner or later.

As it happened, we found out within the next couple of days. A Mahalapi who worked for Adriaan Geel told us. And then we realized how difficult Org Losper's work was. And we no longer envied him his government job – even though it had been especially created for him.

If you know the Mtosas, you'll understand why Org Losper's job was so hard. For instance there was only one member of the whole Mtosa tribe who had ever had any close contact with white men. And he had unfortunately grown up among Trekboers, whose last piece of crockery that they had brought with them from the Cape had got broken almost a generation earlier.

We felt that the Department of Defence could have made an easier job for Org Losper than to send him round asking those questions of the Mtosas, they who did not even know what ordinary kitchen saucers were, leave alone flying ones.

News Story

'The way the world is today,' At Naudé said, shaking his head. 'I don't know what is going to happen.'

From that it was clear that At Naudé had been hearing news over the wireless again that made him fear for the future of the country. We did not exactly sit up, then. We in the Dwarsberge knew that it was the wireless that made At Naudé that way. And he could tremble as much as he liked for the country's future or his own. There was never any change, either, in the kind of news he would bring us. Every time it was about stone-throwings in Johannesburg locations and about how many new kinds of bombs the Russians had got, and about how many people had gone to gaol for telling the Russians about still other kinds of bombs they could make. Although it did not look as though the Russians *needed* to be educated much in that line.

And we could never really understand why At Naudé listened at all. We hardly ever listened to *him*, for that matter. We would rather hear from Gysbert van Tonder if it was true that the ouderling at Pilanesberg really forgot himself in the way that Jurie Steyn's wife had heard about from a kraal Mtosa at the kitchen door. The Mtosa had come to buy halfpenny stamps to stick on his forehead for the yearly Ndlolo dance. Now, there was news for you. About the ouderling, I mean. And even to hear that the Ndlolo dance was being held soon again was at least something. And if it should turn out that what was being said about the Pilanesberg ouderling was not true, well, then, the same thing applied to a lot of what At Naudé heard over the wireless also.

'I don't know what is going to happen,' At Naudé repeated, 'the way the world is today. I just heard over the wireless . . .'

'That's how the news we got in the old days was better,' Oupa

Bekker said. 'I mean in the real old days, when there was no wireless, and there was not the telegraph, either. The news you got then you could do something with. And you didn't have to go to the post office and get it from a newspaper. The post office is the curse of the Transvaal . . .'

Jurie Steyn said that Oupa Bekker was quite right, there. He himself would never have taken on the job of postmaster at Drogevlei if he had as much as guessed that there were four separate forms that he would have to fill in, each of them different, just for a simple five-shilling money order. It was so much brainier and neater, Jurie Steyn said, for people who wanted to send five shillings somewhere, if they would just wrap up a couple of half-crowns in a thick wad of brown paper and then post them in the ordinary way, like a letter. That was what the new red pillar-box in front of his door was *for*, Jurie Steyn explained. The authorities had gone to the expense of that new pillar-box in order to help the public. And yet you still found people coming in for postal orders and money orders. The other day a man even came in and asked could he telegraph some money, somewhere.

'I gave that man a piece of brown paper and showed him the pillar-box,' Jurie Steyn said. 'It seemed, until then, that he did not know what kind of progress we had been making here. I therefore asked him if I could show him some more ways in regard to how advanced the Groot Marico was getting. But he said, no, the indications I had already given him were plenty.'

Jurie Steyn said that he thought it was handsome of the man to have spoken up for the Marico like that, seeing that he was quite a newcomer to these parts.

Because we never knew how long Jurie Steyn would be when once he got on the subject of his work, we were glad when Johnny Coen asked Oupa Bekker to explain some more to us about how they got news in the old days. We were all pleased, that is, except At Naudé, who had again tried to get in a remark but had got no further than to say that if we knew something we would all shiver in our veldskoens.

'How did we get news?' Oupa Bekker said, replying to another question of Johnny Coen's. 'Well, you would be standing in the lands, say, and then one of the Bechuanas would point to a small cloud of dust in the poort, and you would walk across to the big tree by the dam, where the road bends, and the traveller would come past there, with two vos horses in front of his Cape cart, and he would get off from the cart and shake hands and say he was Du Plessis. And you would say you were Bekker, and he would say, afterwards, that he couldn't stay the night on your farm, because he had to get to Tsalala's Kop. Well, there was *news*. You could talk about it for days. For weeks even. You have got no idea how often my wife and I discussed it. And we knew everything that there was to know about the man. We knew his name was Du Plessis.'

At Naudé said, then, that he did not think much of that sort of news. People must have been a bit *simpel* in the head, in those old times that Oupa Bekker was talking about if they thought anything about that sort of news. Why, if you compared it with what the radio announcer said, only yesterday . . .

Jurie Steyn's wife came in from the kitchen at that moment. There was a light of excitement in her eyes. And when she spoke it was to none of us in particular.

'It has just occurred to me,' Jurie Steyn's wife said, 'that is, if it's *true* what they are saying about the Pilanesberg ouderling, of course. Well, it has just struck me that, when he forgot himself in the way they say – provided that he *did* forget himself like that, mind you – well, perhaps the ouderling didn't know that anybody was looking.'

That was a possibility that had not so far occurred to us, and we discussed it at some length. In between our talk At Naudé was blurting out something about the rays from a still newer kind of bomb that would kill you right in the middle of the veld and through fifty feet of concrete. So we said, of course, that the best thing to do would be to keep a pretty safe distance away from concrete, with those sort of rays about, if concrete was as dangerous as all that.

We were in no mood for foolishness. Oupa Bekker took this as an encouragement for him to go on.

'Or another day,' Oupa Bekker continued, 'you would again be standing in your lands, say, or sitting, even, if there was a long day of ploughing ahead, and you did not want to tire yourself out unnecessarily. You would be sitting on a stone in the shade of a tree, say, and you would think to yourself how lazy those Bechuanas look, going backwards and forwards, backwards and forwards, with the plough and the oxen, and you would get quite sleepy, say, thinking to yourself how lazy those Bechuanas are. If it wasn't for the oxen to keep them going, they wouldn't do any work at all, you might perhaps think.

'And then, without your in the least expecting it, you would again have news. And the news would find a stone for himself and come along and sit down right next to you. It would be the new veld-kornet, say. And why nobody saw any dust in the poort, that time, was because the veld-kornet didn't come along the road. And you would make a joke with him and say: "I suppose that's why they call you a *veld*-kornet, because you don't travel along the road, but you come by the veld-*langers*." And the veld-kornet would laugh and ask you a few questions, and he would tell you that they had good rains at Derdepoort . . . Well, there was something that I could tell my wife over and over again, for weeks. It was news. For weeks I had that to think about. The visit of the veld-kornet. In the old days it was real news.'

We could see, from the way At Naudé was fidgeting in his chair, that he guessed we were just egging the old man on to talk in order to scoff at all the important European news that At Naudé regularly retailed to us, and that we were getting tired of.

After a while At Naudé could no longer contain himself.

'This second-childhood drivel that Oupa Bekker is talking,' At Naudé announced, not looking at anybody in particular, but saying it to all of us, in the way Jurie Steyn's wife had spoken when she came out of the kitchen. 'Well, I would actually sooner listen to scandal about the Pilanesberg ouderling. There is at least some sort of meaning to it. I am not being unfriendly to Oupa Bekker, of course. I know it's just that he's old. But it's also quite clear to me that he doesn't know what news *is*, at all.'

Jurie Steyn said that it was at least as sensible as a man lying on the veld under fifty feet of concrete because of some rays. If a man were to lie under fifty feet of concrete he wouldn't be able to breathe, leave alone anything else.

In the meantime, Johnny Coen had been asking Oupa Bekker to tell us some more.

'On another day, say,' Oupa Bekker would go on, 'you would not be in your lands at all, but you would be sitting on your front stoep, drinking coffee, say. And the Cape cart with the two vos horses in front would be coming down the road again, but in the opposite direction, going *towards* the poort, this time. And you would not see much of Du Plessis' face, because his hat would be pulled over his eyes. And the veld-kornet would be sitting on the Cape cart next to him, say.'

Oupa Bekker paused. He paused for quite a while, too, holding a lighted match cupped over his pipe as though he was out on the veld where there was wind, and puffing vigorously.

'And my wife and I would go on talking about it for years afterwards, say,' Oupa Bekker went on. 'For years after Du Plessis was hanged, I mean.'

Lost City

'It used to be different, in the Kalahari,' Chris Welman said, commenting on At Naudé's announcement of what he had heard over the wireless. 'You could go for miles and miles, and it would be just desert. All you'd come across, perhaps, would be a couple of families of Bushmen, and they'd be disappearing over the horizon. Then, days later, you'd again come across a couple of families of Bushmen. And *they'd* be disappearing over the horizon.

'And you wouldn't know if it was the same couple of families of Bushmen. Or the same horizon. And you wouldn't care, either. I mean, in the Kalahari desert you wouldn't care. Maybe in other deserts it is different. I'm only talking about the Kalahari.'

Yes, all you would be concerned about, in the Kalahari, Jurie Steyn said, was what the couple of families of Bushmen would be disappearing over the horizon *with*. For you might not always be able to check up quickly to find out what was missing out of your camp.

'But from what At Naudé has been telling us,' Chris Welman went on, 'it looks like you'd have no quiet in the Kalahari today. Or room to move. From Malopolole onwards it seems that there's just one expedition on top of another, each one searching for a lost city. And you can't slip out for a glass of pontac, even, in case when you come back somebody else has taken your place in the line.'

It was apparent that Chris Welman was drawing on his memory of some past unhappy visit to Johannesburg.

'It's not hard to think of how that city got lost in the first place,' Jurie Steyn observed. 'It must have been that the people that built the city didn't know what a couple of families of Bushmen were like. Still, I can't believe it, somehow, quite. Not a whole city, that is. I can't somehow imagine Bushmen disappearing over the horizon with all that. For one thing, it wouldn't be any use to them. Now, if it wasn't so much a question of a whole lost city, but of some of the things that got lost *out* of the city – well, I could tell those expeditions just where to go and look.'

But At Naudé said that we had perhaps misunderstood one or two of the less important details of the news he had communicated to us. There weren't quite as many expeditions as what Chris Welman seemed to think, out in the Kalahari looking for a lost city. Moreover, it wasn't a city that had got lost in the way that Jurie Steyn meant by lost. The city had just been built so many years ago that people had afterwards forgotten about it. Don't ask him how a thing like that could happen, now, At Naudé said. He admitted that he couldn't imagine it, himself.

'I mean, let's not take even a city –' At Naudé started to explain.

'No, let a few Bushman families take it,' Jurie Steyn said promptly, 'with the washing hanging on the clothes-lines and all.'

'Not a city, even,' At Naudé continued, pointedly ignoring Jurie Steyn's second attempt that afternoon at being what he thought funny, 'but if we think of quite a small town, like Bekkersdal, say . . . Not that I won't agree that we've got a wider water furrow in the main street of Bekkersdal than they've got in Zeerust, of course. But it's only that there are less people *in* the main street of Bekkersdal than they've got in Zeerust, if you understand what I mean . . . Well, can you imagine anybody in Bekkersdal forgetting where they built the place? After all, anybody can see for himself how silly that sounds. It's like Dominee Welthagen, just before the Nagmaal, suddenly forgetting where the church is. Or David Policansky not remembering where his shop is, just after he's done it all up for the New Year.'

We acknowledged that At Naudé was right there, of course. With Dominee Welthagen we might not perhaps be too sure. For it was known that in some respects the dominee could at times be pretty absent-minded. But with David Policansky At Naudé was on safe enough ground. Especially after that new big plate-glass window that David Policansky had put in. It was not reasonable to think that he would be able to forget it. Not with what he was still likely to be owing on it, we said. You just weren't allowed to forget anything you were owing on.

'So you see how much more silly it is with a city, then,' At Naudé concluded. 'Thinking that people would go and build a city, and then just lose it.'

Thereupon young Vermaak, the schoolmaster, said that he had learnt in history of how for many centuries people believed that there was a foreign city called Monomotapa in these parts, and that numbers of expeditions had been sent out in the past to look for it. It was even marked on maps, long ago, the schoolmaster said. But if you saw that name on a map of Africa today, he said, well, then you would know that it wasn't a very up-to-date map of Africa.

As likely as not, there would not be the town of Vanderbijl Park marked on that map, young Vermaak said, laughing. Or the town of Odendaalsrus, even. There was supposed to be a lot of gold and diamonds in that city with the foreign name, the schoolmaster added.

Well, with those remarks young Vermaak broached a subject with which we were not altogether unfamiliar. More than one of us had, before today, held in his hand a map showing as clearly as anything with a cross the exact spot where the hidden treasure would be found buried. And all we'd be likely to dig up there would be an old jam tin. The apocryphal element in African cartography was something we had had experience of.

'All I can say,' Gysbert van Tonder observed at this stage, 'is that I don't know so much about a lost city. But it seems to me there's going to be more than one lost expedition. Depending on how far the expeditions are going into the desert beyond Kang-Kang.'

Several of us looked surprised when Gysbert van Tonder said that. Surprised and also impressed. We knew that in his time

Gysbert van Tonder had penetrated pretty deeply into the Kalahari, bartering beads and brass-wire for cattle. That was, of course, before the Natives in those parts found that they didn't need those things, any more, since they could buy their clothes readymade at the Indian store at Ramoutsa. Nevertheless, we had not imagined that he had gone as far into the desert as all that.

'But is there –' Jurie Steyn inquired after a pause, 'is there really a place by that name, though?'

Gysbert van Tonder smiled.

'On the map, yes,' he said, 'it is. On the map in my youngest son's school atlas you can read that name for yourself there, big as anything. And in the middle of the Kalahari. Well, there's something one of those expeditions can go and look for. And maybe that is their lost city. At least, it's lost enough. Because you certainly won't be able to tell it from any other spot in the Kalahari that you're standing in the middle of, watching a couple of families of Bushmen disappearing over the horizon from.'

So Jurie Steyn said, yes, he reckoned that if it was a lost city that an expedition was after, why, then he reckoned that just about any part of the Kalahari would do for that. Because when the expedition came back from the Kalahari without having found anything, it would prove to the whole world just how lost that city actually was, Jurie Steyn reckoned. If that was what an expedition into the Kalahari was for, then that expedition just couldn't go wrong. In fact, the less that an expedition like that found, then, the better. Because it would show that the city had been lost without as much as a trace, even, Jurie Steyn added.

'It's a queer thing, though,' the schoolmaster said, 'when you come to think of it, that for so many hundreds of years, when the interior of South Africa was still unexplored, there should have been a legend of a Golden City. And people were so convinced of the existence of this city that they went searching for it. They were so sure that there was that city of gold that they even marked it on their maps. And what seems so extraordinary to me is that one day that Golden City actually would arise, and not too far away, either, from where the old geographers had centuries before indicated on their maps. It was as though they were all prophesying the rise of Johannesburg. And at most they were only a few hundred miles out.'

That was something that passed his comprehension, young Vermaak said. That men should have been able to mark on a map, centuries beforehand, a city that was not there yet. That to him was one of the mysteries of Africa, the schoolmaster declared.

Thereupon Oupa Bekker said that if it was a thing like that, that the schoolmaster thought wonderful, then the schoolmaster would have a lot to learn, still.

'After all, with South Africa so big,' Oupa Bekker said, 'they were bound to go and build cities in it, somewhere. That stands to reason. And so, for a person to go and put a mark on a map and to say that some day there is going to be a city there, or thereabouts – well, what would have been wonderful was if it *didn't* work out, some time. And to say that it's surprising how that man made that mark on the map centuries ago, even. Well, I think that only shows how bad he was at it. If Johannesburg got started soon after he had prophesied it, then there might have been something in it, then. But it seems to me that the man who made that map wasn't only a few hundred miles out, as Meneer Vermaak says, but that he was also a few hundred years out. What's more, he also got the name wrong. Unless you also think that that name – what's it, again –'

'Monomotapa,' young Vermaak announced.

'– isn't far out from sounding like Johannesburg,' Oupa Bekker said.

It made him think of his grand-uncle Toons, all this, Oupa Bekker said.

Now, there was something that really did come as a surprise to us. The general feeling we had about Oupa Bekker was a feeling of immense antiquity, of green and immemorial age. In the lost olden-time cities that our talk was about we could, without thinking twice, accord to Oupa Bekker the rights of a venerable citizenship. And in that crumbled town we could conceive of Oupa Bekker as walking about in the evening, among cobwebbed monuments.

It was foolish, of course, to have ideas like that. But that was the impression, in point of appearance and personality, that Oupa Bekker did make on us. He seemed to belong with the battered although timeless antique. He occupied a place not so much among living humanity as in oral tradition.

And so when Oupa Bekker spoke of himself as having had a grand-uncle, it just about took our breath away.

'You were saying about your grand-uncle?' Jurie Steyn, who was the first to recover, remarked. From the tone in his voice, you could see that Jurie Steyn pictured Oupa Bekker's grand-uncle as a lost city in himself, with weeds clambering over his ruined walls.

'My grand-uncle Toons,' Oupa Bekker continued, unaware of the stir he had caused, 'also had the habit, when he first trekked into the Transvaal that was all just open veld, then, of stopping every so often and looking around him and saying that one day a great city would arise right there where he was standing, when it was now just empty veld. On his way up, when he trekked into the Northern Transvaal, he stopped to say it at where is today Potchefstroom and also at where is today Johannesburg and Pretoria. In that way you could say that he was just as good as the man that did that map. And I suppose he was, too. That is, if you don't count all those hundreds of other places where my grand-uncle Toons also stopped to say the same thing, and where there is today still just open veld.'

It was Jurie Steyn who brought the conversation back to where we had started from.

'Those expeditions going to search for the lost city,' he asked of At Naudé, 'have they set out yet? And do you know if they are likely to pass this way, at all? Because, if it's last letters they want to send home, and so on, then my post office is as good as any. I mean, their last letters have got a good chance of getting to where they are addressed to. I don't say the expeditions have got the same chance of getting to the lost city. But instead of taking all that trouble, why don't they just drop a letter in the post to the lost city – writing to the mayor, say? Then they'll at least know if the lost city is there or not.'

But At Naudé said that from what he had heard over the wireless the expeditions were on the point of leaving, or had already left, Johannesburg. And from what Jurie Steyn had said about writing letters – well, he had the feeling that more than one letter that he had himself posted had ended up there, in that lost city.

'Johannesburg?' Oupa Bekker queried, talking as though he was emerging from a dream. 'Well, I've been in Johannesburg only a few times. Like with the Show, say. And I've passed through there on the way to Cape Town. And I've always tried to pull down the curtains of the compartment I was in when we went through Johannesburg. And I have thought of the Good Book, then.

'And I have thought that if ever there was a lost city, it was Johannesburg, I have thought. *And how lost,* I have thought . . . The expedition doesn't need to leave Johannesburg, if it's a lost city it wants.'

Singular Events

What actually *started* the discussion in Jurie Steyn's post office that day was afterwards not very clear. For that matter, it was not too clear, either, afterwards, as to how it all ended. At Naudé did make reference, of course, to a story that he had listened in to over the wireless. But he only brought in that wireless story to illustrate something that somebody else had already said. It had to do with a ship or a boat on which there were a lot of seamen and they were drifting about for a very long time, unable to reach land, At Naudé explained. When At Naudé explained further that it was something that had happened ever so long ago, we felt that he was taking our conversation off its course, in much the same way that the seamen he spoke about had been taken off *their* course, drifting about and all like that on the ocean.

That kind of thing naturally set Oupa Bekker off talking about another ship that couldn't make port. And even before Oupa Bekker spoke we knew what was coming. It was an established fact, as far as you liked to go north of the Dwarsberge, that Oupa Bekker on his grandmother's side was directly descended from Kapitein Van der Decken, jolly skipper in the service of the Dutch East India Company's merchant navy, whose square-rigged brig, a familiar sight off the southern Cape Peninsula, had with the passing years acquired the stage name of *Flying Dutchman*.

We had heard this story so often before from Oupa Bekker that Gysbert van Tonder began heading him off the moment Oupa Bekker brought up his heel to knock out his pipe against. Gysbert van Tonder was only partially successful, however. Oupa Bekker did get so far as to acquaint us once more with some of the details of his last visit to Cape Town.

'Big white sails, just like you see in pictures,' Oupa Bekker concluded. 'And it gave me a lot of pleasure, you understand, to be able to be there at Camp's Bay and to wave at my ancestor. And when I thought of how old *he* was I didn't feel so old any more, somehow, myself. And on the way back to the Transvaal I told a young man in my compartment about it. The young man was a student going home for the holidays, and he had a solemn look, and he said our nation must "Hou koers" and he seemed older, somehow, than me, or even than Kapitein Van der Decken, who is my ancestor on my grandmother's side.'

Seeing that, in spite of our efforts to stop him, Oupa Bekker had actually got so far, Chris Welman, winking at us, decided to humour him.

'And what did that young student say about the Dutch East Indies ship, Oupa,' Chris Welman asked, 'the ship that you stood on the sand and waved at?'

'Oh, you could see that that student knew a thing or two, all right,' Oupa Bekker said. 'The student was very fine about it. He said that the *Flying Dutchman* was a myth. *Mities*, he said it was – just like that. And so I said to him that that was just how I felt about it, too. It was a word I hadn't heard before, I told him. But that was exactly the feeling I had, standing there at Camp's Bay and waving, first with my hand and then with my hat, also. I felt it was just *mities*. And I don't care who knows it, I said to the student.'

Oupa Bekker went on to say that when that student alighted at his destination, which was at a siding somewhere in the Karoo, then the student looked a good few years older, even, than when he had got into the train at Stellenbosch. Older and more solemn, Oupa Bekker remarked. And he glanced over his shoulder, too, once, cautiously, as though suspicious that Oupa Bekker might decide to get off there, also.

It was Jurie Steyn who reminded us of what we had really been discussing. He reminded us in that prim and precise tone of voice that he had started adopting ever since the post-office authorities had erected a strip of brass wire netting over half the length of his counter, thereby bringing Jurie Steyn into line with the post office at Bekkersdal. And now that, for half his length, Jurie Steyn was in line with the Bekkersdal post-office counter, Jurie Steyn frequently spoke in the way that the Bekkersdal postmaster spoke when he pulled down his little green curtain behind the wire netting and told the people waiting in the queue that that section was closed until nine o'clock next morning. Of course, Jurie Steyn didn't make use of that strip of wire netting. For one thing, he didn't have a little green curtain behind it that he could pull down. And, for another thing, even if he did have a curtain, you could always put your head round that part of the counter where there was no wire netting, and *see* Jurie Steyn standing there.

'Anyway, what I want to know,' Jurie Steyn declared, in his new voice of higher officialdom, 'is how we have come to be talking about Oupa Bekker's old ghost ship. As far as I can recall –'

'It's not a ghost ship,' Oupa Bekker asserted. 'If you think you know better than that student –'

'Ghost ship,' Jurie Steyn continued. 'And what's more –'

'Student of divinity, too' – Oupa Bekker chanced his arm – 'And Kapitein Van der Decken was my grandmother's great –'

'Now I remember what we were talking about,' Jurie Steyn announced triumphantly. 'We were talking about the meat shortage in the cities and about all the different kinds of meat that's being cut into strips and hung out on a line to dry for biltong. Baboons, I remember we said. And donkeys. They say there are lots of people in the cities can't tell the difference, when it's biltong. If it's some kind of taste that they haven't had before, then they think, oh, it must be ostrich. They never think it might be donkey. Isn't that what you were telling us, At?'

But At Naudé said, no, he hadn't been discussing that side of the question at all. That was what Chris Welman had been saying, At Naudé explained. He himself had been talking, he said, about that story he had heard over the wireless, about those sailors ever so long ago that were adrift for months and months in a boat miles and miles away from land. That was all *he* said, At Naudé made clear, at the same time expressing the hope that Jurie Steyn wasn't going to get him wrong, now.

This time Oupa Bekker did lean forward, and in such a manner that, whether he wanted to or not, Jurie Steyn had to listen to him.

'Can you tell the difference by the taste, Jurie – now, just by the taste, mind,' Oupa Bekker asked, 'between, say, blesbok biltong and donkey biltong? Because, if you can, *it means you have tasted donkey biltong*. Perhaps you will now tell us when, and where, you *ate* donkey biltong. You know what I mean, strips of donkey hung out on a line to dry, when there's a hot sun, with naeltjies and red pepper.'

Well, that was a fair enough question. All the same, we felt that Oupa Bekker need not have been so nasty about it – particularly in his going to the extent of explaining to Jurie Steyn what biltong was, as though Jurie Steyn didn't know. Well, we felt that Jurie would have been quite within his rights if he had said that Oupa Bekker looked pretty much like a long, unappetizing strip of biltong himself, and without coriander spice in it.

But Jurie Steyn didn't say that. It was almost as though Jurie had sensed that Oupa Bekker wanted him to say that. Jurie was cunning, that way. Accordingly, 'Have *you* eaten donkey biltong, Oupa?' was all that Jurie Steyn would reply, then.

Oupa Bekker paused, with his pipe in the air, looking thoughtful.

'I can't say for sure,' he admitted at length. 'I mean, when people hand you a strip of donkey biltong, they don't tell you it's donkey biltong, do they? Or that it's baboon biltong, either, for that matter – do they, now?'

We agreed that Oupa Bekker was right, there, of course. Not one of us could recall having had a statement of that description made to him just off-hand, sort of.

'And so there it is,' Oupa Bekker announced. 'I may have – I just wouldn't know. But it's silly when people try and explain to you that they can tell by the taste what sort of biltong is what. You can try and guess, of course, but as likely as not you'll be wrong.'

All the same, Oupa Bekker went on, looking doubtful, he couldn't understand how all this kind of talk had come about in the first place. It seemed a bit mixed-up to him, Oupa Bekker added.

'The sailors adrift on that ship,' he said. 'And donkey biltong. And Van der Decken being my ancestor on my grandmother's side –'

We could see that an idea had suddenly occurred to him.

'Oh, yes,' Oupa Bekker said, 'I remember now. It was the biltong we had at Chief Ndlambe's kraal, when Gert Pretorius and I were the first white men to trek into these parts. And although Chief Ndlambe asked us to guess what kind of biltong it was, Gert and I just couldn't. And afterwards Gert Pretorius and I discussed the peculiar way Chief Ndlambe had laughed when we said it was a kind of taste we hadn't really come across before, we didn't think . . . Well, I know now what it is that made me think of my grandmother. Because of the strange stories we heard from the Mtosas later on about Chief Ndlambe's grandmother. About the bitter kinds of disputes she had been having with her grandson, lately, and of how she suddenly disappeared, one day, from the tribal councils. Yes, that part of it I can see quite clearly. But what have those sailors got to do with it – drifting around for months and months on that ship At Naudé has been telling us about?'

Why, it was exactly the same thing, At Naudé said.

Those sailors, At Naudé said, had to eat.

Detective Story

The radio mystery serial to which he had been listening in over a considerable period had, At Naudé informed us, now come to an end. It appeared that the denouement was eminently satisfactory.

'I wouldn't have missed that last instalment for anything,' At Naudé said. 'It's so clever the way everything gets explained – you've got no idea. Right through the serial everybody thinks that the lawyer did it, because of the cigar stompie the police found in the garden. But in the end it turns out that it was a Mshangaan mine-boy who had the regular habit of smoking cigars.

'Clever, hey? What's more, nobody even knew that there was that Mshangaan mine-boy until the very last instalment. Until the last couple of minutes, almost, you can say. Another thing was that the detective was getting secret information all the time from a girl that the leader of the jewel thieves was in love with. And the detective didn't let on about that, either, right until the last instalment. What do you think of that for smart, now? Because it was *secret* information, he kept it secret from everybody.'

We said we wondered what they would think of next. We also said that it sounded very mixed up and clever.

'Yes, you couldn't make head or tail out of it, really,' At Naudé agreed. 'And after it was over there was a bar or two of music and the man who gives the scientific talks was saying a long thing about the latest laboratory research into some stuff that sounded like erughurugh, the way he pronounced it, and –'

'Is it,' Gysbert van Tonder asked, his eye lighting up, 'any good to drink?'

'I don't know,' At Naudé replied, 'but I listened quite a long way into that talk before I realized that it wasn't part of the serial. That's how the last instalment got me, if you understand what I mean.'

*

The schoolmaster said that, from the sound of it, he didn't judge it to be such a good detective serial. The idea of detective fiction was to give the audience an equal chance with the detective of solving the mystery, he said. The audience had to be in possession of all the facts. Whereas, if the detective kept all the clues to himself it was only natural that he should be able to solve the mystery before anybody else.

At Naudé said that would be a fine to-do.

'Why, it's only in the last instalment that the detective produces the blood-stained handkerchief with the crook's initials on it that he picked up at the scene of the crime, and that he didn't mention anything about to a soul,' At Naudé said. 'What did you expect him to do – tell everybody and so put the criminal on his guard?'

Yes, we were all surprised that young Vermaak, who was supposed to be educated and all, and taught school as high as standard four, should have so little understanding as to what a detective radio story was all about.

'It doesn't even need to be over the wireless,' Jurie Steyn said to the schoolmaster. 'You can just *read* that sort of thing, too, week by week.'

He then proceeded to acquaint us with some of the details of a serial he had once followed in a woman's paper to which his wife had subscribed because of a weekly feature in it called 'The Intimate Lives of Celebrated Women Poisoners'.

He never got to the end of the serial, Jurie Steyn said, because his wife stopped taking that paper when the Women Poisoners articles finished and they ran a series, instead, that was entitled 'Woman, the Ministering Angel' – the first article dealing with how to treat smallpox in your own home on veld or vlei.

'But what I remember most about that mystery serial,' Jurie Steyn said, 'was the unusual sort of detective they had in it. The person that questioned all the suspects and carried out the detective investigations was only doing it in a spare-time way. His real job was being the sword swallower in a circus.'

*

That started Chris Welman off telling us about the time a friend of his, Joggem Dieder, who was then living in the Wolmaransstad district, got a sudden thirst for adventure. And he ran away from home to join a circus. Joggem was then aged sixty-three.

'We talked a lot about it among ourselves,' Chris Welman said, 'and we used to make jokes about Joggem Dieder riding horses, standing on the saddle on one leg. Or we would picture him, his old limbs creaking, flying high up in the air on a swing, with a plug of chew tobacco in his cheek.'

But from the few letters that Joggem Dieder wrote back, Chris Welman said, it would appear that he was happy in his new career and that he had adapted himself successfully to the wild life of the circus.

'All the same, we were a bit disappointed when the circus came to Wolmaransstad and we found that Joggem didn't take part in any of the big performances, but was only in a sideshow,' Chris Welman said. 'In fact, we hardly recognized him when we first saw him, him all dressed up in a silk frock and a yellow wig, and a hat with flowers and a blue feather, and smiling in a silly way. And his dress was arranged so that you couldn't see his feet. And so Joggem Dieder made quite a good Bearded Woman. I mean, he always *had* one of the longest beards in the district.'

Oupa Bekker had been waiting for some time for a chance to talk.

'The neatest bit of detective work I ever saw,' Oupa Bekker said, 'also had in it a circus performer. But *he* did juggling and rope tricks. Afterwards he left the circus and became a bywoner on Neels Prinsloo's farm. And when Neels Prinsloo was one morning found hanging on a tree on the way to the cattle-kraal the veld-kornet that came along worked out a solution to the affair that was so well thought out that people were still talking about it for months afterwards.

'The neighbour who saw Neels Prinsloo hanging from the tree just took one look and then went and fetched other neighbours.

'The neighbours knew they hadn't to touch anything. So, when the veld-kornet arrived, it was to find Neels Prinsloo still hanging from the tree and a man with a shot-gun standing guard over the bywoner, in case, with his circus training, he got out of the riems they had tied him up with. For they were convinced that the bywoner had murdered Neels Prinsloo and had then hung him from the tree to make it look like suicide.

'The veld-kornet took a rapid survey of the situation. "Unknot them both," he ordered.

'It appeared that the rope under Neels Prinsloo's chin had been tied with a kind of slipknot that the bywoner was known to make – something he had brought with him from the circus. Another thing was that Neels Prinsloo's feet were dangling eighteen inches above the ground and there was nothing underneath that he could have stood on.

'Even if Neels Prinsloo was a circus acrobat himself – which he was far from being, with his lumbago – he couldn't possibly have tied his neck so high up from the ground like that without help. Finally, the bywoner had frequently, and in the presence of witnesses, threatened to murder Neels Prinsloo. The bywoner's last threat had been uttered only the day before.

'But the veld-kornet freed the bywoner from the net of suspicion quicker than the farmers were able to get Neels Prinsloo down from the tree, on account of the circus knot.

'"How long has the bywoner been on this farm?" the veld-kornet asked. Two years, they told him. "Well, Neels Prinsloo was one of the most progressive farmers in these parts," the veld-kornet said. "He no doubt learnt from the bywoner how to make that kind of knot.

'"Now, you say Neels Prinsloo had nothing to stand on when he hanged himself. What time was he found hanging?" They told him, at daybreak. "Milking time," the veld-kornet said. "That means that he stood on an upturned bucket and a Mchopi, passing down this foot-path on his way to work, took the pail along with him, to the kraal. Eighteen inches is just the height of a milking pail. And the Mchopi wouldn't have seen Neels Prinsloo hanging from the tree, because the Mchopi would have had his eyes down on the ground, all the time, looking for dagga."

'"Now about those threats," the veld-kornet went on. "Has there ever been a farm in the Transvaal where a bywoner does not regularly threaten to murder the farmer he works for?"'

That was Oupa Bekker's story of the brilliant piece of real life detective work on the part of the veld-kornet. But it was a story that didn't carry conviction, somehow.

'What was more,' Oupa Bekker went on, as though sensing our scepticism, 'why the veld-kornet was so sure of himself was because he had received a letter from Neels Prinsloo, saying he was going to hang himself, because he was sick of the government. That was why the veld-kornet got to the farm so early, before he had been sent for – because he had Neels Prinsloo's letter.'

We still looked doubtful. It wasn't a story that rang true, somehow, take it how you liked. Oupa Bekker coughed.

'They also found a Mchopi who admitted picking up a bucket just there that he took to the kraal for milking,' Oupa Bekker declared, stoutly. 'Just like the veld-kornet worked out.'

Still there was silence. Then Oupa Bekker played his trump card – which had the unfortunate effect of leaving us more incredulous than ever.

'*When Neels Prinsloo came round*,' Oupa Bekker said, 'he *confirmed* that everything the veld-kornet said was correct.'

At This Time of Year

It was always about now, Jurie Steyn said, with the year drawing to an end, that he got all sorts of queer feelings. He didn't know how to say them, quite. But one feeling he did get, and that he had no difficulty in explaining, he said, was a homesickness to be back again in the Western Province where he had spent his early childhood.

Jurie Steyn heaved a medium-length sigh, then, thinking back on the years when he was young.

'Not that I haven't got a deep love for the Transvaal,' Jurie Steyn added, in case we should get him wrong, 'I am, after all, a Transvaler –'

And so we said, yes, it was quite all right. We understood his feelings for the old Cape Colony. He needn't explain, we said.

'And because I've said that I passed my young years in the Cape,' Jurie Steyn went on, the suggestion of a combative look coming into his eye, 'that doesn't mean to say that I am old, today.'

We hastened to reassure him on that point, too – but not very convincingly, it seemed. Gysbert van Tonder even coughed.

'I know what you mean, Jurie,' young Johnny Coen said, quickly, hastening to forestall any unpleasantness that might ensue on Jurie Steyn demanding of Gysbert van Tonder what he meant by clearing his throat, that way. 'It's the place where you were born and bred and you can't ever forget. I was born in the Marico bushveld, and you've got no idea how homesick I got the time I was working on the railway at Ottoshoop.

'But, of course, Ottoshoop is at least ninety miles from here – further even, if you don't go the road through Sephton's Nek. So I know how you feel, Jurie. No matter how kind people are to you, even, if they're not your own people you do get very lonely, sometimes. Oh, yes, I went through all that at Ottoshoop.'

Johnny Coen went on to describe a wedding reception that he had attended at Ottoshoop while he was an exile in those parts.

'They had spread white tablecloths over long tables on the front stoep,' Johnny Coen said. 'And there was a man at the party who did balancing tricks with a chair and a wine-glass. And I got more and more sad. The only time I laughed a little was when the loose seat dropped out of the chair and caught the man on the back of his neck when he was at the same time throwing up two guavas and a fork.'

Johnny Coen went on to say that, as it turned out, his neighbour at table was also a foreigner.

'How I knew,' Johnny Coen said, 'was when that man spoke to me. And he said I was looking pretty miserable. And he asked was it that I was in love with the bride, perhaps, and that another man had taken her away from me. And I said, no, I was from the Dwarsberge part of Marico, and I felt most homesick for Groot Marico when the people around me were most happy, I said. And that was how I got talking to that Englishman sitting next to me at the table. And when somebody in the voorkamer started playing "Home, Sweet Home" on the harmonium we were both of us crying on to the tablecloth. And I never used to think that an Englishman had any feelings, until then.

'Another thing I found out afterwards that I had in common with the Englishman was that he didn't like that man with the balancing tricks, either.'

Thereupon Jurie Steyn said that he, too, wouldn't like it very much if somebody were to start playing 'Home, Sweet Home' on a harmonium at this time of the year. Of course, he knew it best as a German song, Jurie Steyn said, and it was called 'Heimat Susse Heimat'. But the tune was the same. He had heard the German missionaries at Kronendal sing it quite often. And they would cry on to the thick slices of that kind of red sausage that they had on their plates, Jurie said.

*

'Take the Cape at this time of the year, now,' Jurie Steyn said, 'in the summer.'

So we said, very well, we would take the Cape, then, if he put it like that.

'Well, when it gets towards about now, towards about Christmas time and the end of the year,' Jurie Steyn proceeded, 'why, I just can't help it. I think of a little Boland dorp with white houses and water furrows at the side of the streets and oak-trees. Not that I haven't got all the time in the world for a moepel or a maroela or a kremetart or any other kind of bushveld tree. For instance, I have often walked to the end of my farm by the poort, just to go and look at the withaaks there. No, it isn't that. After all, an oak isn't a proper South African tree, even, but just imported.

'All the same, when it gets towards Christmas, the thought of those oak-trees in the Cape comes into my mind just all of a sudden, sort of. And I get the feeling of how much nobler a kind of person I was in those days than what I am today. I think of how much more upright I was in my youth.'

Thereupon Gysbert van Tonder said, yes, *that* he could well believe.

We knew that Gysbert van Tonder – who was Jurie Steyn's neighbour – was hinting about the last bit of neighbourly unpleasantness they had, which had to do with the impounding of a number of stray oxen. And we didn't want to have *that* long argument all over again. Especially not with the Christmas season drawing near, and all.

It was quite a good thing, therefore, that Oupa Bekker should have started talking then about a quite ordinary camel-thorn tree that grew on one end of Bekkersdal when it was first laid out as a dorp.

'It was because of what Jurie Steyn said about oaks that made me think of it,' Oupa Bekker said. 'I was there when Bekkersdal was proclaimed as a township, and the bush was cleared away and the surveyor measured out the streets and divided up the erfs. And the commandant-general and the dominee had words about whether the plein in the middle of the dorp should be for the Dopper Church, with a pastorie next to it, or for the Dopper Church, with a house for the commandant-general's son-in-law next to it, a site to be chosen for the pastorie that would be within easy walking distance for the dominee.'

Oupa Bekker said that in the end the dominee decided that he wouldn't mind walking a little distance. Oupa Bekker said he had no doubt that what made the dominee come to that decision was because the dominee did not wish to make the commandant-general unhappy.

For it was well known throughout the Northern Transvaal that few things made the commandant-general so unhappy as when he had to take firm steps against anybody who opposed him. And Oupa Bekker said it was also known that on occasion the commandant-general had taken steps that you might call even unusually firm against a person who stood in his way.

'And so the dominee agreed, in the end,' Oupa Bekker continued, 'that a short brisk walk from his pastorie to the church, of a Sunday morning before the sermon, would be healthful for him. And so a house for the commandant-general was built on the measured-out erf on the plein next to the church. But all that happened – oh, so many years ago.'

Oupa Bekker's sigh would have been more prolonged than Jurie Steyn's had been. Only, because of his advanced years, Oupa Bekker didn't have the breath for it.

'All the same, that was a funny thing,' Chris Welman commented, 'for the old days, that is. And so I suppose that's the reason why –'

Oupa Bekker nodded.

For we knew where the pastorie was, today, in Bekkersdal. And we knew that the present-day minister, Dominee Welthagen, had to walk a fairish distance to the church, of a Sunday, just as his predecessor of three-quarters of a century ago had to do. But that first dominee would no doubt have been able to take short cuts, since at that time Bekkersdal would not have been as built up as it was today.

'And that erf that was measured out for the commandant-general's son-in-law –' Chris Welman started to remark.

'Yes, that's the reason for all that trouble there, now,' Oupa Bekker said. 'But the old people always knew that the commandant-general's son-in-law was a bit thoughtless. All those empty bottles that used to lie in his backyard, for instance. And that backyard isn't any more tidy today. Not with all those empty jam tins and all that garbage and all those empty fruit boxes lying in it. Why, that backyard looks worse than ever, now that it has been taken over for an Indian store. And right next to the Dopper Church, and all. No wonder there's that trouble about it in Bekkersdal, now.'

So we said, it was very sinful of the first Indian – who was the grandfather of the present Indian – to have gone and bought that erf right next to the Dopper Church to go and open an Indian store on.

There should really have been a pastorie there, we said.

'Bit of a pity the commandant-general's son drank so much,' Johnny Coen observed.

In the discussion that followed about what a scandal it was that there should be an Indian store next to the Dopper Church in Bekkersdal, Oupa Bekker was able only in an edgeways fashion to tell us about the camel-thorn tree that grew at the edge of the Bekkersdal township. And we were not able to pay much attention to Oupa Bekker's story, then. Whereas it was quite a pretty story.

It appears that the streets of the newly laid dorp were planted with jacarandas – an imported tree then coming into fashion. And at the end of one street, in exact line with the jacarandas, and at the same distance from its nearest jacaranda neighbour as the jacarandas were set apart from each other, there grew that indigenous old African camel-thorn tree.

And although the street ended just before it came to him, the old camel-thorn tree really imagined that he was part of that jacaranda avenue. And he was as pleased as anything about it. And he started putting on side, there, just as though he was also an imported tree, and not just an old camel-thorn that the veld was full of. And even though the municipality didn't water him, like they watered the jacaranda, the camel-thorn remained as cheerful as ever. He knew he didn't *need* watering.

Anyway, the point of Oupa Bekker's story had to do with the first summer that the jacarandas in Bekkersdal came to flowering. And one night there was a terrible wind from the Kalahari, so that in the morning the sidewalks were thickly strewn with purple flowers, and there were more jacaranda blooms stuck on the thorns of the old camel-thorn tree than any jacaranda still had on its branches, then. And the purple blossoms lay thick about the lower part of the gnarled trunk of the camel-thorn. It was his hour, and so you couldn't tell him from an imported tree.

We didn't hear very much of what Oupa Bekker had to say, however. We were too busy thinking out the right words for a strong letter we were drafting to our Member in Parliament. It had to do with the Indian Problem.

But it was after the railway lorry from Bekkersdal had drawn up at the front door that Gysbert van Tonder really let himself go on the Indian Problem. It was when Gysbert found out that the roll of barbed wire he had ordered wasn't on the lorry.

'It's the fault of the Indian storekeeper's assistant,' the lorry driver explained – although he used a different word in referring to the young Indian who was helping the old Indian in the Bekkersdal store. 'I could see that the young Indian assistant wasn't himself. The shop was all done out with Christmas stockings, and things. And that old gramophone they've got at the back of the shop was playing "Home, Sweet Home". And that young Indian assistant was busy crying on to the counter.

'Saying that at this time of the year he always got homesick for Natal, the Indian assistant said. Well, that beats me, all right. How anybody can ever feel homesick for Natal, I just don't know.'

A Bekkersdal Marathon

At Naudé, who had a wireless set, came into Jurie Steyn's voorkamer, where we were sitting waiting for the railway lorry from Bekkersdal, and gave us the latest news. He said that the newest thing in Europe was that young people there were going in for non-stop dancing. It was called marathon dancing, At Naudé told us, and those young people were trying to break the record for who could remain on their feet longest, dancing.

We listened for a while to what At Naudé had to say, and then we suddenly remembered a marathon event that had taken place in the little dorp of Bekkersdal – almost in our midst, you could say. What was more, there were quite a number of us sitting in Jurie Steyn's post office, who had actually taken part in that non-stop affair, and without knowing that we were breaking records, and without expecting any sort of a prize for it, either.

We discussed that affair at considerable length and from all angles, and we were still talking about it when the lorry came. And we agreed that it had been in several respects an unusual occurrence. We also agreed that it was questionable if we could have carried off things so successfully that day, if it had not been for Billy Robertse.

You see, our organist at Bekkersdal was Billy Robertse. He had once been a sailor and had come to the bushveld some years before, travelling on foot. His belongings, fastened in a red handkerchief, were slung over his shoulder on a stick. Billy Robertse was journeying in that fashion for the sake of his health. He suffered from an unfortunate complaint for which he had at regular intervals to drink something out of a black bottle that he always carried handy in his jacket pocket.

Billy Robertse would even keep that bottle beside him in the organist's gallery in case of a sudden attack. And if the hymn the predikant gave out had many verses, you could be sure that about halfway through Billy Robertse would bring the bottle up to his mouth, leaning sideways towards what was in it. And he would put several extra twirls into the second part of the hymn.

When he first applied for the position of organist in the Bekkersdal church, Billy Robertse told the meeting of deacons that he had learnt to play the organ in a cathedral in Northern Europe. Several deacons felt, then, that they could not favour his application. They said that the cathedral sounded too Papist, the way Billy Robertse described it, with a dome three hundred feet high and with marble apostles. But it was lucky for Billy Robertse that he was able to mention, at the following combined meeting of elders and deacons, that he had also played the piano in a South American dance hall, of which the manager was a Presbyterian. He asked the meeting to overlook his unfortunate past, saying that he had had a hard life, and anybody could make mistakes. In any case, he had never cared much for the Romish atmosphere of the cathedral, he said, and had been happier in the dance hall.

In the end, Billy Robertse got the appointment. But in his sermons for several Sundays after that the predikant, Dominee Welthagen, spoke very strongly against the evils of dance halls. He described those places of awful sin in such burning words that at least one young man went to see Billy Robertse, privately, with a view to taking lessons in playing the piano.

But Billy Robertse was a good musician. And he took a deep interest in his work. And he said that when he sat down on the organist's stool behind the pulpit, and his fingers were flying over the keyboards, and he was pulling out the stops, and his feet were pressing down the notes that sent the deep bass tones through the pipes – then he felt that he could play all day, he said.

I don't suppose he guessed that he would one day be put to the test, however.

It all happened through Dominee Welthagen one Sunday morning going into a trance in the pulpit. And we did not realize that he was in a trance. It was an illness that overtook him in a strange and sudden fashion.

At each service the predikant, after reading a passage from the Bible, would lean forward with his hand on the pulpit rail and give out the number of the hymn we had to sing. For years his manner of conducting the service had been exactly the same. He would say, for instance: 'We will now sing Psalm 82, verses 1 to 4.' Then he would allow his head to sink forward on to his chest and he would remain rigid, as though in prayer, until the last notes of the hymn died away in the church.

Now, on that particular morning, just after he had announced the number of the psalm, without mentioning what verses, Dominee Welthagen again took a firm grip on the pulpit rail and allowed his head to sink forward on to his breast. We did not realize that he had fallen into a trance of a peculiar character that kept his body standing upright while his mind was a blank. We learnt that only later.

In the meantime, while the organ was playing over the opening bars, we began to realize that Dominee Welthagen had not indicated how many verses we had to sing. But he would discover his mistake, we thought, after we had been singing for a few minutes.

All the same, one or two of the younger members of the congregation did titter, slightly, when they took up their hymn books. For Dominee Welthagen had given out Psalm 119. And everybody knows that Psalm 119 has 176 verses.

This was a church service that will never be forgotten in Bekkersdal.

We sang the first verse and then the second and then the third. When we got to about the sixth verse and the minister still gave no sign that it would be the last, we assumed that he wished us to sing the first eight verses. For, if you open your hymn book, you'll see that Psalm 119 is divided into sets of eight verses, each ending with the word 'Pouse'.

We ended the last notes of verse eight with more than an ordinary number of turns and twirls, confident that at any moment Dominee Welthagen would raise his head and let us know that we could sing 'Amen'.

It was when the organ started up very slowly and solemnly with the music for verse nine that a real feeling of disquiet overcame the congregation. But, of course, we gave no sign of what went on in our minds. We held Dominee Welthagen in too much veneration.

Nevertheless, I would rather not say too much about our feelings, when verse followed verse and Pouse succeeded Pouse, and still Dominee Welthagen made no sign that we had sung long enough, or that there was anything unusual in what he was demanding of us.

After they had recovered from their first surprise, the members of the church council conducted themselves in a most exemplary manner. Elders and deacons tiptoed up and down the aisles, whispering words of reassurance to such members of the congregation, men as well as women, who gave signs of wanting to panic.

At one stage it looked as though we were going to have trouble from the organist. That was when Billy Robertse, at the end of the 34th verse, held up his black bottle and signalled quietly to the elders to indicate that his medicine was finished. At the end of the 35th verse he made signals of a less quiet character, and again at the end of the 36th verse. That was when Elder Landsman tiptoed out of the church and went round to the Konsistorie, where the Nagmaal wine was kept. When Elder Landsman came back into the church he had a long black bottle half-hidden under his manel. He took the bottle up to the organist's gallery, still walking on tiptoe.

At verse 61 there was almost a breakdown. That was when a message came from the back of the organ, where Koster Claassen and the assistant verger, whose task it was to turn the handle that kept the organ supplied with wind, were in a state near to exhaustion. So it was Deacon Cronjé's turn to go tiptoeing out of the church. Deacon Cronjé was head warder at the local gaol. When he came back it was with three burly Native convicts in striped jerseys, who also went through the church on tiptoe. They arrived just in time to take over the handle from Koster Claassen and the assistant verger.

At verse 98 the organist again started making signals about his medicine. Once more Elder Landsman went round to the Konsistorie. This time he was accompanied by another elder and a deacon, and they stayed away somewhat longer than the time when Elder Landsman had gone on his own. On their return the deacon bumped into a small hymn book table at the back of the church. Perhaps it was because the deacon was a fat, red-faced man, and not used to tiptoeing.

At verse 124 the organist signalled again, and the same three members of the church council filed out to the Konsistorie, the deacon walking in front this time.

It was about then that the pastor of the Full Gospel Apostolic Faith Church, about whom Dominee Welthagen had in the past used almost as strong language as about the Pope, came up to the front gate of the church to see what was afoot. He lived near our church and, having heard the same hymn tune being played over and over for about eight hours, he was a very amazed man. Then he saw the door of the Konsistorie open, and two elders and a deacon coming out, walking on tiptoe – they having apparently forgotten that they were not in church, then. When the pastor saw one of the elders hiding a black bottle under his manel, a look of understanding came over his features. The pastor walked off, shaking his head.

At verse 152 the organist signalled again. This time Elder Landsman and the other elder went out alone. The deacon stayed behind on the deacon's bench, apparently in deep thought. The organist signalled again, for the last time, at verse 169. So you can imagine how many visits the two elders made to the Konsistorie altogether.

The last verse came, and the last line of the last verse. This time it had to be 'Amen'. Nothing could stop it. I would rather not describe the state that the congregation was in. And by then the three Native convicts, red stripes and all, were, in the Bakhatla tongue, threatening mutiny. 'Aa-m-e-e-n' came from what sounded like less than a score of voices, hoarse with singing.

The organ music ceased.

Maybe it was the sudden silence that at last brought Dominee Welthagen out of his long trance. He raised his head and looked slowly about him. His gaze travelled over his congregation and then looking at the windows, he saw that it was night. We understood right away what was going on in Dominee Welthagen's mind. He thought he had just come into the pulpit, and that this was the beginning of the evening service. We realized that, during all the time we had been singing, the predikant had been in a state of unconsciousness.

Once again Dominee Welthagen took a firm grip of the pulpit rail. His head again started drooping forward on to his breast. But before he went into a trance for the second time, he gave out the hymn for the evening service. 'We will,' Dominee Welthagen announced, 'sing Psalm 119.'

Laugh, Clown, Laugh

'It's the clown,' Johnny Coen said, starting to laugh all over again. 'The tall clown in the fancy dress – yellow and blue and the smart way of walking. I could go to the circus and see it all through again, just to laugh at that clown. He kept a straight face even when they chucked the bucket of water over him. It was a real scream to see his new clothes getting all soaked . . . oh, *soaked*. And he went on standing there in the middle of the ring as solemn as you like, not being able to make out where the water came from, even.'

Johnny Coen laughed as though he was seeing all that happening again, right in front of his eyes, and for the first time.

But Oupa Bekker said that what he liked best at the circus were the elephants. The way they stood on their hind-legs and the way they walked on bottles, Oupa Bekker said, balancing themselves to music.

'It's years ago since I was last able to balance *myself* to music,' Oupa Bekker continued, 'leave alone walk on bottles.'

'Or stand on your hind-legs,' Jurie Steyn commented – not loud enough for Oupa Bekker to hear, though.

In the old days there wasn't any such thing in the Transvaal, Oupa Bekker went on, as walking on bottles. Even though the whole of the Marico up to the Limpopo was elephant country in those days, Oupa Bekker said – and, in consequence, he prided himself on knowing something of the habits of elephants – he would never have imagined their walking on bottles.

If an elephant had seen a bottle in his path he would simply have walked over it. To him an elephant in those days was just an elephant, Oupa Bekker said.

And the same thing applied to lions, when the Groot Marico was lion country, Oupa Bekker added. To him a lion was just a *lion*, and not a bookish person that – that, well, we all saw what those lions *did* at the circus, didn't we, now? There was more than one white man in this part of the Marico that wasn't nearly as well educated as some of those circus lions, Oupa Bekker said.

Of course, he acknowledged that not every white person in this part of the Marico had had those same opportunities of schooling as the lions had.

Then At Naudé said that what he just couldn't get over, at the circus at Bekkersdal, were the trained zebras.

'And to think that this was also zebra country,' At Naudé remarked. 'But I would never have imagined a zebra wearing a red ostrich feather on his head, just like he's a Koranna Bushman. Or a zebra, while galloping down to the water-hole, first stopping to write something on a blackboard with chalk.'

We spoke also about other animals that we had seen at the circus, and we said that the Groot Marico had at one time been that kind of animals' country, too. And all the time we had never known what those animals were really like. That sort of thing made you think, we said.

When Jurie Steyn was talking about the mule we had seen at the circus, that could jump six feet, and Jurie was saying that the Groot Marico was also mule country, Gysbert van Tonder suddenly gave a short laugh.

'And the clowns, that Johnny Coen was mentioning,' Gysbert van Tonder said. 'Well, it seems to me that for a pretty long while the Marico has been good clown country. And still is.'

That was something that made you think, too, didn't it? – Gysbert van Tonder asked.

We were more than a little surprised, at a remark like that coming from Gysbert van Tonder. And several of us told him that we thought he should be the last person to talk. We proceeded to give Gysbert van Tonder some sound reasons, too, as to why we believed he should be the last person to talk. And some of the reasons we gave him had to do with things that hadn't happened so long ago, either.

This discussion would probably have gone on for quite a while, with each of us being able to think up a fresh reason every few minutes, when Chris Welman started talking about the fine insouciance with which the red-coated ringmaster cracked his whip.

The ringmaster didn't look very particular as to whether it was the gaily caparisoned horse he hit, or the blonde equestrienne hanging head downwards from the saddle, her golden locks trailing in the sawdust – so it seemed to Chris Welman, anyway.

'She didn't once stop smiling, either,' Chris Welman said, 'all the time the music played.'

From the way Chris Welman spoke, it was apparent that, in the sounds discoursed by the circus band, his ear detected no harsh dissonances. Nor to his eye did the set smile of the equestrienne convey any suggestion of artifice. It was, however, significant, that in his unconscious mind he had, indeed, established a link between those two circus reciprocals – the music's blare and the set smile.

'After the circus was over and I had got back home, I was still thinking of her a long time,' Chris Welman said. 'I thought of her a good way into the night. I thought of her with the electric light on her hair, hanging down on the ground, and her spitting out the sawdust every time that it came into her mouth from the way she was riding, hanging down.'

It was obvious that Chris Welman had occupied a ringside seat.

'But mostly I thought of her, about what she was doing after the show was over,' Chris Welman said. 'I pictured her there under that tent, locked up alone in her cage. It must be an unnatural sort of life, I thought, for a girl.' And he winked.

We were able to put Chris Welman right on that point, however.

It wasn't that we had any sort of inside knowledge of circus life, of course, but we just went by common sense. It was only the more wild kind of performers in a circus that got locked in cages, we said. The tamer ones just got knee-haltered, we said, or tied to stakes with riems. So he was quite wrong in thinking of the blonde equestrienne as having to be locked in a cage after the show was over, we told Chris Welman. Likely as not they even let her go loose, we said. And we also winked.

Thereupon At Naudé said that that was the trouble.

And after we had pondered At Naudé's remark carefully, we realized that there was much truth in it.

A pretty girl, we said, if she was wild enough, was a lot more dangerous than any kind of lion. And no matter how fiercely the lion might roar, either, we said. Because all a pretty girl needed to do was to lower her eyelashes in a particular way, we said. And for that she did not have to be an equestrienne or an equilibriste or anything else, we added.

It was only natural, after that, that the talk should turn on the subject of pretty girls in general. And it was still more natural that, before we knew where we were, we should be discussing Pauline Gerber.

What made it somewhat difficult for us to talk as freely as we would have liked about what we had been hearing of Pauline Gerber lately, was the fact that Johnny Coen was there, sitting in Jurie Steyn's voorkamer.

And we knew full well how Johnny Coen had felt about Pauline Gerber, both before she went to the finishing school in the Cape, and after she came back from the finishing school.

As it happened, however, Johnny Coen helped us out, to some extent, and perhaps without knowing it, even.

Gysbert van Tonder had just made the admission that, in so far as he was able to judge, Pauline Gerber was not only just the prettiest girl in this part of the Marico bushveld, but also the most attractive. 'If you know what I mean by *attractive*,' Gysbert van Tonder had added. 'Otherwise I could tell you –'

That was when Johnny Coen had interrupted Gysbert van Tonder.

'No, no, you don't need to tell us,' Johnny Coen said, hastily, 'not in words, and all that. And not when it's – when it's Pauline Gerber, I should say. You've told us things like that before today. About what you find attractive in girls, that is. And so if you perhaps don't say it all over again, we won't feel that we have missed anything. Because you've said it all *before*, that is.'

After a few moments' reflection, Gysbert van Tonder conceded Johnny Coen's point. He had spoken on that subject quite a good bit, he acknowledged, but there was still just this one thing he wanted to say –

'Not now, please,' Johnny Coen interjected. And he spoke so sharply, and with such unwonted heat, that Gysbert van Tonder shut up, looking slightly puzzled, all the same.

'I was only going to *say* –' Gysbert van Tonder concluded in an aggrieved tone, and left it at that. For if Johnny Coen was going to act funny, and so on, well, it was not a matter for him, Gysbert van Tonder, to have to go out of his way to help Johnny right.

'Well, I've only seen Pauline Gerber a few times, since she's been back from finishing school,' Johnny Coen said. And from the way he said 'few' we knew that he wanted us to think that it meant more than, say, exactly twice.

But, of course, we weren't really interested in the number of times that Johnny Coen had seen Pauline Gerber of late. What we were anxious to learn was how often the young schoolmaster, Vermaak, had been seeing her. For it was in relation to young Vermaak, and not to Johnny Coen, that a certain amount of talk was going on about Pauline Gerber.

'Well, the few times that I have seen her,' Johnny Coen went on, 'it was a bit difficult for me to know what to think, exactly. The first time I saw her the schoolmaster had just left. And the second time – I mean, *on another occasion* when I saw her at her house, she was sort of expecting Meneer Vermaak to come round. But what I want to say is that what Chris Welman said about the circus girl – why, that is exactly what I *feel* about Pauline Gerber. About how pretty she is, and all that. And what makes it still more queer is that she talks about herself like Chris Welman talks about the girl that rides in the circus.

'She feels she's shut up in a *cage*, Pauline Gerber says. To have to live here in the bushveld, with everybody so narrow-minded, Pauline Gerber says, is like being shut up in a cage.'

Johnny Coen went on at considerable length, after that, acquainting us with the true nature of the sentiments he entertained for Pauline Gerber. But we were not interested. We did not in any way doubt the purity or sincerity of his feelings. Only, we were not concerned with all that. What we really wanted to know was what was going on between Pauline Gerber and the young schoolmaster. And it was apparent that Johnny Coen couldn't tell us more than what we already knew. It was a pity that Johnny Coen should be struck with such blindness, though, we thought. It would be better if the scales were to drop from Johnny Coen's eyes, we felt.

It was Oupa Bekker who brought the talk back to a discussion of the circus – which was, after all, where we had started from.

'Walking *on* bottles,' Oupa Bekker was saying. 'Well, that's a new one on me. And I've known the Marico when it was elephant country. Unless, maybe, it was giraffe country. And what a giraffe would look like, standing on his hind-legs, I just can't think of, right away.'

That was what gave Johnny Coen his chance to get back to the clowns, once more.

'The one clown poured water from a step-ladder out of a bucket on to that other clown that I was telling you about,' Johnny Coen said. 'And I just about laughed my head off, each time, to see how that other clown got soaked. And they had Natives to come running in from the back entrance with more buckets of water. And it all went over that clown. I enjoyed it more than I enjoyed the Chinese acrobat, even, who jumped through two wheels with knives in them. And all the time that clown didn't know what was happening. Every time I saw a Native come running in with another bucket of water, why I just about *died*, laughing.'

We gazed at Johnny Coen pretty steadily, as he spoke. And we thought of what was going on between Pauline Gerber and young Vermaak, the schoolmaster. And all the time Johnny Coen went on feeling the way he did about Pauline. And we wondered if Gysbert van Tonder had been so far wrong, when he said that this was clown country.

The tears started coming into Johnny Coen's eyes, eventually, the way he was laughing about that clown.

Play within a Play

'But what did Jacques le Français want to put a thing like that on *for*?' Gysbert van Tonder asked.

In those words he conveyed something of what we all felt about the latest play with which the famous Afrikaans actor, Jacques le Français, was touring the platteland. A good number of us had gone over to Bekkersdal to attend the play. But – as always happens in such cases – those who hadn't actually seen the play knew just as much about it as those who had. More, even, sometimes.

'What I can't understand is how the kerkraad allowed Jacques le Français to hire the church hall for a show like that,' Chris Welman said. 'Especially when you think that the church hall is little more than a stone's throw from the church itself.'

Naturally, Jurie Steyn could not let that statement pass. Criticism of the church council implied also a certain measure of fault-finding with Deacon Kirstein, who was a first cousin of Jurie's wife.

'You can hardly call it a stone's throw,' Jurie Steyn declared. 'After all, the plein is on two morgen of ground and the church hall is at the furthest end from the church itself. And there is also a row of bluegums in between. Tall, well-grown bluegums. No, you can hardly call all that a stone's throw, Chris.'

So At Naudé said that what had no doubt happened was that Jacques le Français with his insinuating play-actor ways had got round the members of the kerkraad, somehow. With lies, as likely as not. Maybe he had told the deacons and elders that he was going to put on that play *Ander Man se Kind* again, which everybody approved of, seeing it was so instructive, the relentless way in which it showed up the sinful life led in the great city of Johannesburg and in which the girl in the play, Baba Haasbroek, got ensnared, because she was young and from the backveld, and didn't know any better.

'Although I don't know if that play did any good, really,' At Naudé added, thoughtfully. 'I mean, it was shortly after that that Drieka Basson of Enzelsberg left for Johannesburg, wasn't it? Perhaps the play *Ander Man se Kind* was a bit too – well – relentless.'

Thereupon Johnny Coen took a hand in the conversation.

It seemed very long ago, the time Johnny Coen had gone to Johannesburg because of a girl that was alone there in that great city. And on his return to the Marico he had not spoken much of his visit, beyond mentioning that there were two men carved in stone holding up the doorway of a building near the station and that the pavements were so crowded that you could hardly walk on them. But for a good while after that he had looked more lonely in Jurie Steyn's voorkamer than any stranger could look in a great city.

'I don't know if you can say that that play of Jacques le Français' about the girl that went to Johannesburg really is so very instructive,' Johnny Coen said. 'There are certain things in it that are very true, of course. But there are also true things that could never go into one of Jacques le Français' plays – or into any play, I think.'

Gysbert van Tonder started to laugh, then. It was a short sort of a laugh.

'I remember what you said when you came back from Johannesburg, that time,' Gysbert van Tonder said to Johnny Coen. 'You said the pavements were so crowded that there was hardly room to walk. Well, in the play, *Ander Man se Kind,* it wasn't like that. The girl in the play, Baba Haasbroek, didn't seem to have trouble to walk about on the pavement. I mean, half the time, in the play, she was walking on the pavement. Or if she wasn't walking she was standing under a street lamp.'

It was then that At Naudé mentioned the girl in the new play that Jacques le Français had put on at Bekkersdal. Her name was

Truida Ziemers. It was a made-up name, of course, At Naudé said. Just like Jacques le Français was a made-up name. His real name was Poggenpoel, or something. But how any Afrikaans writer could *write* a thing like that . . .

'It wasn't written by an Afrikaans dramatist,' young Vermaak, the school-teacher, explained. 'It is a translation from . . .'

'To think that any Afrikaner should fall so low as to *translate* a thing like that, then,' Gysbert van Tonder interrupted him. 'And what's more, Jacques le Français or Jacobus Poggenpoel, or whatever his name is, is Coloured. I could see he was Coloured. No matter how he tried to make himself up, and all, to look White, it was a Coloured man walking about there on the stage. How I didn't notice it in the play *Ander Man se Kind* I don't know. Maybe I sat too near the back, that time.'

Young Vermaak did not know, of course, to what extent we were pulling his leg. He shook his head sadly. Then he started to explain, in a patient sort of a way, that Jacques le Français was actually *playing* the role of a Coloured man. He wasn't supposed to be White. It was an important part in the unfolding of the drama that Jacques le Français wasn't a White man. It told you all that in the title of the play, the schoolmaster said.

'What's he then, a Frenchman?' Jurie Steyn asked. 'Why didn't they say so, straight out?'

Several of us said after that, each in turn, that there was something you couldn't understand, now. That a pretty girl like Truida Ziemers, with a blue flower in her hat, should fall in love with a Coloured man, and even marry him. Because that was what happened in the play.

'And it wasn't as though she didn't know,' Chris Welman remarked. 'Meneer Vermaak has just told us that it says it in the title of the play, and all. Of course, I didn't see the play myself. I meant to go, but at the last moment one of my mules took sick. But I saw Truida Ziemers on the stage, once. And even now, as I am talking about her again, I can remember how pretty she was.

And to think that she went and married a Coloured man when all the time she *knew*. And it wasn't as though he could tell her that it was just sunburn, seeing that she could read it for herself on the posters. If the schoolmaster could read it, so could Truida.'

Anyway, that was only to be expected, Gysbert van Tonder said. That Jacques le Français would murder Truida Ziemers in the end, he meant. After all, what else could you expect from a marriage like that? Maybe from that point of view the play could be taken as a warning to every respectable White girl in the country.

'But that isn't the *point* of the play,' young Vermaak insisted, once more. 'Actually, it *is* a good play. And it is a play with real educational value. But not that kind of educational value. If I tell you that this play is a translation – (and a pretty poor translation, too: I wouldn't be surprised if Jacques le Français translated it himself) – of the work of the great . . .'

This time the interruption came from Johnny Coen.

'It's all very well talking like they have been doing about a girl going wrong,' Johnny Coen said. 'But a great deal depends on circumstances. That is something I have learnt, now. Take the case now of a girl that . . .'

We all sat up to listen, then. And Gysbert van Tonder nudged Chris Welman in the ribs for coughing. We did not wish to miss a word.

'A girl that . . . ?' At Naudé repeated in a tone of deep understanding, to encourage Johnny Coen to continue.

'Well, take a girl like that girl Baba Haasbroek in the play, *Ander Man se Kind*,' Johnny Coen said. Jurie Steyn groaned. We didn't want to hear all *that*, over again.

'Well, anyway, if that girl *did* go wrong,' Johnny Coen proceeded – pretty diffidently, now, as though he could sense our feelings of being balked – 'then there might be reasons for it. Reasons that didn't come out in the play, maybe. And reasons that we sitting here in Jurie Steyn's voorkamer would perhaps not have the right to judge about, either.'

*

Gysbert van Tonder started clearing his throat as though for another short laugh. But he seemed to change his mind halfway through.

'And in this last play, now,' Johnny Coen added, 'if Jacques le Français had really loved the girl, he wouldn't have been so jealous.'

'Yes, it's a pity that Truida Ziemers got murdered in the end, like that,' At Naudé remarked. 'Her friends in the play should have seen what Jacques le Français was up to, and have put the police on to him, in time.'

He said that with a wink, to draw young Vermaak, of course.

Thereupon the schoolmaster explained with much seriousness that such an ending would defeat the whole purpose of the drama. But by that time we had lost all interest in the subject. And when the government lorry came soon afterwards and blew a lot of dust in at the door we made haste to collect our letters and milk-cans.

Consequently, nobody took much notice of what young Vermaak went on to tell us about the man who wrote the play. Not the man who translated it into Afrikaans but the man who wrote it in the first place. He was a writer who used to hold horses' heads in front of a theatre, the schoolmaster said, and when he died he left his second-best bed to his wife, or something.

Birth Certificate

It was when At Naudé told us what he had read in the newspaper about a man who had thought all his life that he was White, and had then discovered that he was Coloured, that the story of Flippus Biljon was called to mind. I mean, we all knew the story of Flippus Biljon. But because it was still early afternoon we did not immediately make mention of Flippus. Instead, we discussed, at considerable length, other instances that were within our knowledge of people who had grown up as one sort of person and had discovered in later life that they were in actual fact quite a different sort of person.

Many of these stories that we recalled in Jurie Steyn's voorkamer as the shadows of the thorn-trees lengthened were based only on hearsay. It was the kind of story that you had heard, as a child, at your grandmother's knee. But your grandmother would never admit, of course, that she had heard that story at *her* grandmother's knee. Oh, no. She could remember very clearly how it all happened, just like it was yesterday. And she could tell you the name of the farm. And the name of the landdrost who was summoned to take note of the extraordinary occurrence, when it had to do with a more unusual sort of changeling, that is. And she would recall the solemn manner in which the landdrost took off his hat when he said that there were many things that were beyond human understanding.

Similarly now, in the voorkamer, when we recalled stories of white children that had been carried off by a Bushman or a baboon or a werewolf, even, and had been brought up in the wilds and without any proper religious instruction, then we also did not think it necessary to explain where we had first heard those stories. We spoke as though we had been actually present at some stage of the affair – more usually at the last scene, where the child, now grown to manhood and needing trousers and a pair of braces and a hat, gets restored to his parents and the magistrate after studying the birth certificate says that there are things in this world that baffle the human mind.

And while the shadows under the thorn-trees grew longer the stories we told in Jurie Steyn's voorkamer grew, if not longer, then, at least, taller.

'But this isn't the point of what I have been trying to explain,' At Naudé interrupted a story of Gysbert van Tonder's that was getting a bit confused in parts, through Gysbert van Tonder not being quite clear as to what a werewolf was. 'When I read that bit in the newspaper I started wondering how must a man *feel*, after he has grown up with adopted parents and he discovers, quite late in life, through seeing his birth certificate for the first time, that he isn't White, after all. That is what I am trying to get at. Supposing Gysbert were to find out suddenly –'

At Naudé pulled himself up short. Maybe there were one or two things about a werewolf that Gysbert van Tonder wasn't too sure about, and he would allow himself to be corrected by Oupa Bekker on such points. But there were certain things he wouldn't stand for.

'All right,' At Naudé said hastily, 'I don't mean Gysbert van Tonder, specially. What I am trying to get at is, how would any one of us feel? How would any White man feel, if he has passed as White all his life, and he sees for the first time, from his birth certificate, that his grandfather was Coloured? I mean, how would he *feel*? Think of that awful moment when he looks in the palm of his hands and he sees . . .'

'He can have that awful moment,' Gysbert van Tonder said. 'I've looked at the palm of my hand. It's a White man's palm. And my fingernails have also got proper half-moons.'

At Naudé said he had never doubted that. No, there was no need for Gysbert van Tonder to come any closer and show him. He could see quite well enough just from where he was sitting. After Chris Welman had pulled Gysbert van Tonder back on to the rusbank by his jacket, counselling him not to do anything foolish, since At Naudé did not mean *him*, Oupa Bekker started talking about a White child in Schweizer-Reneke that had been stolen out of its cradle by a family of baboons.

'I haven't seen that cradle myself,' Oupa Bekker acknowledged, modestly. 'But I met many people who have. After the child had been stolen, neighbours from as far as the Orange River came to look at that cradle. And when they looked at it they admired the particular way that Heilart Nortjé – that was the child's father – had set about making his household furniture, with glued klinkpenne in the joints, and all. But the real interest about the cradle was that it was empty, proving that the child had been stolen by baboons. I remember how one neighbour, who was not on very good terms with Heilart Nortjé, went about the district saying that it could only have *been* baboons.

'But it was many years before Heilart Nortjé and his wife saw their child again. By *saw*, I mean getting near enough to be able to talk to him and ask him how he was getting on. For he was always too quick, from the way the baboons had brought him up. At intervals Heilart Nortjé and his wife would see the tribe of baboons sitting on a rant, and their son, young Heilart, would be in the company of the baboons. And once, through his field-glasses, Heilart had been able to observe his son for quite a few moments. His son was then engaged in picking up a stone and laying hold of a scorpion that was underneath it. The speed with which his son pulled off the scorpion's sting and proceeded to eat up the rest of the scorpion whole filled the father's heart of Heilart Nortjé with a deep sense of pride.

'I remember how Heilart talked about it. "Real intelligence," Heilart announced with his chest stuck out. "A real baboon couldn't have done it quicker or better. I called my wife, but she was a bit too late. All she could see was him looking as pleased as anything and scratching himself. And my wife and I held hands and we smiled at each other and we asked each other, where does he get it all from?"

'But then there were times again when that tribe of baboons would leave the Schweizer-Reineke area and go deep into the Kalahari, and Heilart Nortjé and his wife would know nothing about what was happening to their son, except through reports from farmers near whose homesteads the baboons had passed. Those farmers had a lot to say about what happened to some of their sheep, not to talk of their mealies and watermelons. And Heilart would be very bitter about those farmers. Begrudging his son a few prickly-pears, he said.

'And it wasn't as though he hadn't made every effort to get his son back, Heilart said, so that he could go to catechism classes, since he was almost of age to be confirmed. He had set all sorts of traps for his son, Heilart said, and he had also thought of shooting the baboons, so that it would be easier, after that, to get his son back. But there was always the danger, firing into a pack like that, of his shooting his own son.'

'The neighbour that I have spoken of before,' Oupa Bekker continued, 'who was not very well disposed towards Heilart Nortjé, said that the real reason Heilart didn't shoot was because he didn't always know – actually *know* – which was his son and which was one of the more flat-headed kees-baboons.'

It seemed that this was going to be a very long story. Several of us started getting restive . . . So Johnny Coen asked Oupa Bekker, in a polite sort of a way, to tell us how it all ended.

'Well, Heilart Nortjé caught his son, afterwards,' Oupa Bekker said. 'But I am not sure if Heilart was altogether pleased about it. His son was so hard to tame. And then the way he caught him. It was with the simplest sort of baboon trap of all . . . Yes, *that* one. A calabash with a hole in it just big enough for you to put your hand in, empty, but that you can't get your hand out of again when you're clutching a fistful of mealies that was put at the bottom of the calabash. Heilart Nortjé never got over that, really. He felt it was a very shameful thing that had happened to him. The thought that his son, in whom he had taken so much pride, should have allowed himself to be caught in the simplest form of monkey-trap.'

When Oupa Bekker paused, Jurie Steyn said that it was indeed a sad story, and it was no doubt, perfectly true. There was just a certain tone in Jurie Steyn's voice that made Oupa Bekker continue.

'True in every particular,' Oupa Bekker declared, nodding his head a good number of times. 'The landdrost came over to see about it, too. They sent for the landdrost so that he could make a report about it. I was there, that afternoon, in Heilart Nortjé's voorkamer, when the landdrost came. And there were a good number of other people, also. And Heilart Nortjé's son, half-tamed in some ways but still baboon-wild in others, was there also. The landdrost studied the birth certificate very carefully. Then the landdrost said that what he had just been present at surpassed ordinary human understanding. And the landdrost took off his hat in a very solemn fashion.

'We all felt very embarrassed when Heilart Nortjé's son grabbed the hat out of the landdrost's hand and started biting pieces out of the crown.'

When Oupa Bekker said those words it seemed to us like the end of a story. Consequently, we were disappointed when At Naudé started making further mention of that piece of news he had read in the daily paper. So there was nothing else for it but that we had to talk about Flippus Biljon. For Flippus Biljon's case was just the opposite of the case of the man that At Naudé's newspaper wrote about.

Because he had been adopted by a Coloured family, Flippus Biljon had always regarded himself as a Coloured man. And then one day, quite by accident, Flippus Biljon saw his birth certificate. And from that birth certificate it was clear that Flippus Biljon was as White as you or I. You can imagine how Flippus Biljon must have felt about it. Especially after he had gone to see the magistrate at Bekkersdal, and the magistrate, after studying the birth certificate, confirmed the fact that Flippus Biljon was a White man.

'Thank you, baas,' Flippus Biljon said. 'Thank you very much, my basie.'

White Ant

Jurie Steyn was rubbing vigorously along the side of his counter with a rag soaked in paraffin. He was also saying things which, afterwards, in calmer moments, he would no doubt regret. When his wife came into the voorkamer with a tin of Cooper's dip, Jurie Steyn stopped using that sort of language and contented himself with observations of a general nature about the hardships of life in the Marico.

'All the same, they are very wonderful creatures, those little white ants,' the schoolmaster remarked. 'Among the books I brought here into the Marico, to read in my spare time, is a book called *The Soul of the White Ant*. Actually, of course, the white ant is not a true ant at all. The right name for the white ant is isoptera –'

Jurie Steyn had another, and shorter, name for the white ant right on the tip of his tongue. And he started saying it, too. Only, he remembered his wife's presence in time, and so he changed the word to something else.

'This isn't the first time the white ants got in behind your counter,' At Naudé announced. 'The last lot of stamps you sold me had little holes eaten all round the edges.'

'That's just perforations,' Jurie Steyn announced. 'All postage stamps are that way. Next time you have got a postage stamp in your hand, just look at it carefully, and you'll see. There's a law about it, or something. In the department we talk of those little holes as perforations. It is what makes it possible for us, in the department, to tear stamps off easily, without having to use a scissors. Of course, it's not everybody that knows that.'

At Naudé looked as much hurt as surprised.

'You mustn't think I am *so* ignorant, Jurie,' he announced severely. 'Mind you, I'm not saying that, perhaps, when this post office was first opened, and you were still new to affairs, and you couldn't be expected to *know* about perforations and things, coming to this job raw, from behind the plough – I'm not saying that you mightn't have cut the stamps loose with a scissors or a Number 3 pruning shears, even. At the start, mind you. And nobody would have blamed you for it, either. I mean, nobody ever has blamed you. We've all, in fact, admired the way you took to this work. I spoke to Gysbert van Tonder about it, too, more than once. Indeed, we both admired you. We spoke about how you stood behind that counter. With kraal manure in your hair, and all, just like you were postmaster-general. Bold as brass, we said, too.'

The subtle flattery in At Naudé's speech served to mollify Jurie Steyn.

'You said all that about me?' he asked. 'You did?'

'Yes,' At Naudé proceeded smoothly. 'And we also admired the neat way you learnt to handle the post-office rubber stamp, Gysbert and I. We said you held on to it like it was a branding iron. And we noticed how you would whistle, too, just before bringing the rubber stamp down on a parcel, and how you would step aside afterwards, quickly, just as though you half-expected the parcel to jump up and poke you in the short ribs. To tell you the truth, Jurie, we were *proud* of you.'

Jurie Steyn was visibly touched. And so he said that he admitted he had been perhaps a bit arrogant in the way he had spoken to At Naudé about the perforations. The white ants had got among his postage stamps, Jurie Steyn acknowledged – once. But what they ate you could hardly notice, he said. They just chewed a little around the edges.

But Gysbert van Tonder said that, all the same, that was enough. His youngest daughter was a member of the Sunshine Children's Club of the church magazine in Cape Town, Gysbert said. And his youngest daughter wrote to Aunt Susann, who was the woman editor, to say that it was her birthday. And when Aunt Susann mentioned his youngest daughter's birthday in the Sunshine Club corner of the church magazine, Aunt Susann wrote that she was a little girl staying in the lonely African wilds. Gramadoelas was the word that Aunt Susann used, Gysbert van Tonder said. And all just because Aunt Susann had noticed the way that part of the springbok on the stamp on his youngest daughter's letter had been eaten off by white ants, Gysbert van Tonder said.

He added that his daughter had lost all interest in the Sunshine Children's Club, since then. It sounded so uncivilized, the way Aunt Susann wrote about her.

'As though we're living in a grass hut and a string of crocodiles around it, with their teeth showing,' Gysbert van Tonder said. 'As though it's all still Konsessie farms and we haven't made improvements. And it's no use trying to explain to her, either, that she must just feel sorry for Aunt Susann for not knowing any better. You can't explain things like that to a child.'

Nevertheless, while we all sympathized with Gysbert van Tonder, we had to concede that it was not in any way Jurie Steyn's fault. We had all had experience of white ants, and we knew that, mostly, when you came along with the paraffin and Cooper's dip, it was too late. By the time you saw those little tunnels, which the white ants made by sticking grains of sand together with spit, all the damage had already been done.

The schoolmaster started talking some more about his book dealing with the life of the white ant, then, and he said that it was well known that the termite was the greatest plague of tropic lands. Several of us were able to help the schoolmaster right. As Chris Welman made it clear to him, the Marico was not in the tropics at all. The tropics were quite a long way up. The tropics started beyond Mochudi, even. A land surveyor had established that much for us, a few years ago, on a coloured map. It was loose talk about wilds and gramadoelas and tropics that gave the Marico a bad name, we said. Like with that Aunt Susann of the Sunshine Children's Club. Maybe we did have white ants here – lots of them, too – but we certainly weren't in the tropics, like some countries we knew, and that we could mention, also, if we wanted to. Maybe what had happened was that the white ants had come down here *from* the tropics, we said. From away down beyond Mochudi and other side Frik Bonthuys' farm, even. There *was* tropics for you, now, we said to the schoolmaster. Why, he should just see Frik Bonthuys' shirt. Frik Bonthuys wore his shirt outside of his trousers, and the back part of it hung down almost on to the ground.

The schoolmaster said that he thought we were perhaps just a little too sensitive about this sort of thing. He was interested himself in the white ant, he explained, mainly from the scientific point of view. The white ant belonged to the insect world, that was really very highly civilized, he said. All the insect world didn't have was haemoglobin. The insect had the same blood in his veins as a white man, the schoolmaster said, except for haemoglobin.

Gysbert van Tonder said that whatever that thing was, it was enough. Gysbert said it quite hastily, too. He said that when once you started making allowances for the white ant, that way, the next thing the white ant would want would be to vote. And *he* wouldn't go into a polling booth along side of an ant, to vote, Gysbert van Tonder said, even if that ant *was* white.

This conversation was getting us out of our depths. The talk had taken a wrong turning, but we couldn't make out where, exactly. Consequently, we were all pleased when Oupa Bekker spoke, and made things seem sensible again.

'The worst place I ever knew for white ants, in the old days,' Oupa Bekker said, 'was along the Malopo, just below where it joins the Crocodile River. *There* was white ants for you. I was a transport rider in those days, when all the transport was still by ox-waggon. My partner was Jan Theron. We called him Jan Mankie because of his wooden leg – a back wheel of the ox-waggon having gone over his kneecap one day when he had been drinking mampoer. Anyway, we had camped out beside the Malopo. And next morning, when we inspanned, Jan Mankie was saying how gay and *light* he felt. He couldn't understand it. He even started thinking that it must be the drink again, that was this time affecting him in quite a new way. We didn't know, of course, that it was because the white ants had hollowed out all of his wooden leg while he had lain asleep.

'And what was still more queer was that the waggon, when he inspanned it, also seemed surprisingly light. It didn't strike us what the reason for that was, either, just then. Maybe we were not in a guessing frame of mind, that morning. But when our trek got through the Paradys Poort, into a stiff wind that was blowing across the vlakte, it all became very clear to us. For the sudden cloud of dust that went up was not just dust from the road. Our waggon and its load of planed Oregon pine were carried away in the finest kind of powder you can imagine, and all our oxen were left pulling was the trek-chain. And Jan Mankie Theron was standing on one leg. His other trouser leg, that was of a greyish coloured moleskin, was flapping empty in the wind.'

Thus, Oupa Bekker's factual account of a straightforward Marico incident of long ago, presenting the ways and characteristics of the termite in a positive light, restored us to a sense of current realities.

'But what are you supposed to do about white ants, anyway?' Johnny Coen asked after a while. 'Cooper's dip helps, of course. But there should be a more permanent way of getting rid of them, I'd imagine.'

It was then that we all turned to the schoolmaster, again. What did it say in that book of his about the white ant, we asked him.

Well, there was a chapter in his book on the destruction of termites, the schoolmaster said. At least, there had been a chapter. It was the last chapter in the book. But he had unfortunately left the book lying on his desk in the schoolroom over one weekend. And when he had got back on Monday morning there was a little tunnel running up his desk. And the pages dealing with how to exterminate the white ant had been eaten away.

Day of Wrath

It was what At Naudé had read in the newspapers.

Somewhere in an overseas country the people in that part had come together in a barn to wait for the end of the world, which a holy woman had gone out of her way to prophesy for them would be quite soon.

'They stopped work and sold their land for – well, I don't quite remember, now, how much they *got* for it a morgen,' At Naudé said. 'But it went quite cheap. And so they just sat in the barn, waiting for the Day of Judgement.'

Then Gysbert van Tonder said he wondered what those lands were like that the holy woman's followers had sold. Maybe it was just brak soil, and with ganna bushes. Well, that sort of ground you could *keep*, Gysbert van Tonder said. He had had experience of just that kind of lands. And what about turf soil, now, he asked – the sticky kind? There was a thing for you, too, he observed.

Thereupon Chris Welman said that if those people sitting in that overseas barn, there, wanted land so cheap that it was almost *nothing* a morgen – certainly not more than ten pounds a morgen, with two boreholes thrown in – then he himself was just the right man for them to come and talk to. Did the newspaper give the address of that barn, perhaps?

In the slight altercation that ensued between Gysbert van Tonder and Chris Welman (Gysbert van Tonder contending that he had thought of it first and that Chris Welman had no right to come and intrude, talking about ten pounds a morgen for a piece of koppie that you couldn't keep a goat alive on, not unless you fed the goat an old hat or a piece of shirt, every so often), At Naudé was able to explain, several times, that they had missed the whole point of what he was talking about. It wasn't the price of ground a morgen that the newspaper story dealt with so much as the preparations that those people were making for the Day of Judgement.

'The End of the *World*,' At Naudé stated majestically, 'Die laaste der *dagen*.'

He knew it would sound more solemn if he said it in Bible Nederlands instead of just in Afrikaans.

But by that time Chris Welman was saying to Gysbert van Tonder that Gysbert was pretty much like a goat himself, the way he had come butting in, and Gysbert van Tonder was saying that the way Chris Welman's trousers looked from the back, it would appear as though Gysbert had already been feeding part of his trousers to the goats.

'Anyway, where's your shirt buttons?' Chris Welman asked of Gysbert van Tonder, sarcastically, 'I suppose the ostriches ate them?'

We felt that this was an unfortunate quarrel, between Gysbert van Tonder and Chris Welman. We sensed that it was the kind of argument that wouldn't get either of them anywhere. Moreover, when it came to a matter of dress – or, rather, to a question of tabulating things that weren't there – why, we knew that we were none of us immune from thoughtless criticism.

The jagged missiles that Gysbert van Tonder and Chris Welman were hurling at each other on the score of the respective shortcomings in their personal attire – well, a rusty old piece of that kind of weapon could wound any one of us, sitting in Jurie Steyn's voorkamer. And even if it wasn't aimed at you, and even if it got you only glancingly, it could make you feel bruised, all the same. More than one of us shifted uncomfortably on his riempies chair, then.

But it was when Chris Welman was talking about when Gysbert van Tonder had had a haircut last that Oupa Bekker took a firm hand in the proceedings.

We were more than a little surprised that, in spite of his deafness, Oupa Bekker should have followed the argument so well. We had noticed that about Oupa Bekker before, however – that he didn't really miss much about what was going on: not when he was personally affected, that was.

'At Naudé has been talking about Judgement *Day*,' Oupa Bekker said severely, at the same time moving his good veldskoen forward, so as partly to hide the place in his other veldskoen that was patched with a piece of rubber tubing. 'And on the Day of Judgement we will none of us be judged by the *clothes* we're wearing, at the time. We'll be judged by just what we are.'

From the way Oupa Bekker said it, it sounded that that would be bad enough.

So Chris Welman said that he certainly hoped, for Gysbert van Tonder's own sake, that on the Last Day Gysbert would not be judged by the kind of clothes he was wearing. If Gysbert's clothes already looked like that now, Chris Welman said, he would rather not *think* how they would look on the Last Day. He just couldn't imagine anything more sinful, Chris Welman added. Not just off-hand he couldn't, Chris Welman said.

Before Gysbert van Tonder could think of a suitable answer, Oupa Bekker went on to say that what really was sinful was the way Chris Welman had talked of wanting to sell his ground – asking ten pounds a morgen for it – to those people in a foreign country who didn't know any better.

'Religious people,' Oupa Bekker said. 'Sitting there in a barn because their prophetess woman had told them that it was the End of the World. And Protestant people, too, by the sound of it.'

We agreed with Oupa Bekker that they *were* Protestants, by the sound of it.

'And just because Chris Welman wants to trek to Rhodesia, as we all know,' Oupa Bekker announced, finally, 'he doesn't ask even if they're Catholics, first, before he thinks of selling his farm to them, which we know *isn't* worth ten pounds a morgen, just because he wants to go to Rhodesia.'

*

Chris Welman could only say that for those people to have his farm was better than their sitting in a barn, anyway. Whereupon Gysbert van Tonder said that he wasn't so sure.

Gysbert van Tonder also said that if Chris Welman got ten pounds a morgen for his farm, then it *would* be the end of the world.

Oupa Bekker agreed with Gysbert van Tonder. Oupa Bekker said that he knew Chris Welman's farm in the old days, when it was just concession ground. And he wouldn't be sure if he didn't even *prefer* that ground like it was in the old days, before Chris Welman had made what he called improvements on it, Oupa Bekker added.

It seemed queer that Oupa Bekker should be so very much against Chris Welman. But it was only when Oupa Bekker spoke again that we understood something of the reason for it. And we also realized in a deeper manner the truth of what we had in the course of time come to understand about Oupa Bekker's deafness: that Oupa Bekker was hardly at all deaf when there was talk going on in which he was personally affected.

'Take my own little place, now,' Oupa Bekker said. 'There it lies, on both sides of Pappegaai Poort. *There's* a bit of ground for you, now. For somebody that wants to make a new start, and that isn't afraid of a bit of hard work, Catholic *or* Protestant, *there's* now a –'

But Oupa Bekker didn't get any further. For by that time we were all laughing.

'Well, I only hope that on the Last Day I'm not found on *your* farm, Oupa Bekker,' Chris Welman said. 'Not when it comes to being judged, that is. And no matter what sort of clothes I had on, either. Even if I was wearing my black Nagmaal manel, I wouldn't fancy my chances much, if I was found walking on Judgement Day on any part of your farm. Not with all that khakibos and those erosion sloots, I wouldn't.'

*

All the same, it was strange to think that Oupa Bekker, at his age, should also be toying with the idea of trekking to Rhodesia. Otherwise he would never want to sell his farm. It must be that Oupa Bekker had also heard about how much you could make out of tobacco, in Rhodesia. Perhaps he had also heard about how glad the Rhodesian government was to have Afrikaners trekking in there, so much so that they were asking questions about it in the Rhodesian Legislative Assembly almost every week.

It was only after At Naudé had spoken for some time again, trying to give us a clear picture of that prophetess woman and her followers waiting in the barn in their foreign language for the Last Day, that we began to understand properly what it *meant*.

And we started to think of Gabriel's trumpet, then. And of the book in the tenth chapter of Revelations that St John wrote. And of the millions of people, the dead and the living, that would gather at the foot of Mount Zion. And of the vials of wrath. And the fall of Babylon. And the beast with seven heads.

These were things you could not reflect on just lightly.

'I wonder why they were so quick to listen to their prophet woman, the people in that foreign part,' Jurie Steyn commented at length, scratching his head at the same time. 'I mean, there must have been a reason, why they heeded her words and sold up so quick. After all, there was nothing that she could prophesy to them that could be half as bad as what you can read for yourself in the last few pages of the Good Book. Things like the passing of the first world in pools of fire. I have read it more than once, for myself, in a time of drought. And it has brought me a good deal of comfort, too, in a time of drought.'

Well, we were in entire agreement with Jurie Steyn, there. When there had been no rain in the Marico for three years, we said, and the last water in the borehole was drying up – if you could even call it water, with all that brack in it – well, it was comforting, we acknowledged, to sit on one's front stoep and to read of the Day of Wrath and of the second seal being opened.

It made you feel quite happy, then, we said, to think of all the awful things that were going to happen to the world; and to think that it was all just round the corner, too, from the way the holy St John spoke.

We were suddenly able to understand something of what must have been going on in the minds of those foreign people, who listened to their prophetess woman. Seeing that we were farmers ourselves, we understood.

'I think I see what you're getting at, Jurie,' At Naudé remarked, after a while. 'You get a bellyful of it, sometimes, don't you? After all, even if there isn't a drought, you do suddenly find, when you take a look over your farm, including the improvements you've made on it –'

'Especially the improvements,' Chris Welman interjected bitterly, 'no matter what Oupa Bekker says about them –'

'Anyway, you do get the feeling,' At Naudé continued, 'Revelations or no Revelations – that you've just got a bellyful.'

Until that moment we had not understood, properly, why it was that there was so much solace to be found in the last twenty chapters of the Good Book, ending up with 'der volken daarin brengen'.

If it was the End of the World, then, at least, the End of the World would be a change. And the lure of selling up and going to Rhodesia did not have much to do with tobacco-planting, but it was a thing as old as Africa.

'It's funny, now, about Policansky,' Gysbert van Tonder remarked. 'But the last time I saw David Policansky, he told me he was looking for a buyer for his store. He wanted to trek out somewhere, right away from Bekkersdal, he said. And you know what – from the way that David Policansky spoke, it sounded almost as though he had also been reading the New Testament, for drawing comfort. He wasn't talking much different from what we're talking now. He would sell out quite cheap, he said, too.'

Jim Fish

He was an African from a kraal in the Waterberg, and he had not been in Johannesburg very long. His name was Mletshwa Kusane. That was his name in the kraal in the Waterberg. In Johannesburg he was known as Jim Fish. That name stood on his pass, too. Since it is Christmas, the season of goodwill, Mletshwa Kusane, alias Jim Fish, comes into the story skulking a little.

In those days a black man didn't mind what sort of 'working name' he adopted. He had not come to Johannesburg to stay, anyway. At least that was what he hoped. And while he stayed in the city, saving up money as fast as he could to take back to the farm with him, he didn't particularly care what name his employer chose to bestow on him, provided that his employer handed over his wages with due regularity on pay day.

Jim Fish had found work in a baker's shop in a part of the town known as the Mai-Mai. He lived in a shack behind the bakery, the proprietor of which in this way received back as rent a not inconsiderable part of his employees' emoluments. Since his employees were also his tenants, the owner of the bakehouse did not have to employ a rent-collector. Afterwards, when Johannesburg took on more of the external characteristics of a city, the owner of the bakery was to find that this arrangement did not pay him quite so well, any more. For the City Council began introducing all sorts of finicky by-laws relating to hygiene. In no time they brought in a regulation making it illegal for the owner of a bakery to accommodate his Native services on the bakery premises. The result was that, at a time when business wasn't too good, the owner of the bakery found himself with a municipal health inspector on his pay-roll. Afterwards it was two health inspectors. And they came round every month for their rake-off like clockwork. Because of this increase in his overheads the bakery proprietor had been reluctantly compelled to cancel an advertisement that he had been running in a religious magazine for a long time. It was purely a goodwill advertisement, bread being a staple commodity that didn't require advertising. But on the following Sunday the baker – who was also a sidesman – had to listen to a sermon on the evils of avarice. He knew the parson meant him, of course. Because he had cancelled the ad that for years had been the church magazine's mainstay. But there were moments, in the course of the sermon, when the baker could not, in his sinful mind, help associating words like 'cupidity', 'selfishness' and 'money-grubbing' with those two municipal health inspectors.

Jim Fish's main work at the bakery consisted of helping his black colleagues – there were quite a number of them – to carry in the sacks of meal and to clean the mixers of yesterday's dough. (The mixers *were* cleaned, quite often, in spite of what quite a lot of bread-consuming citizens might have thought, going by the taste.) He had also to carry the pans to the oven, and to help stoke the fires, and to help pull out the baked loaves with long wooden scoops. Because Jim Fish was black, that was about as far as his duties went. The white men on the night shift were there in a supervisory capacity.

There had been one or two nights, however, when Jim Fish and his black-skinned colleagues had, through the machinery breaking down, to perform certain additional duties that brought them into somewhat more intimate contact with the ancient rites of bread-baking. On those occasions that particular bakery's proud boast that its products were, from start to finish, untouched by human hand, was only literally correct, in the sense that it excluded human feet. Strict adherents of the school of thought that places the coloured races outside of the pale of humanity as such would in this situation find themselves in something of a dilemma. For it would not be human hands *or* feet, but just the feet of niggers that kneaded the dough, in long wooden troughs, at those times when the electric power at the bakery failed.

The white supervisors would be in a state of nerves, all right, on a night when there was mechanical trouble. They would be all strung up – hysterical and panicky, almost, like ballet-dancers.

'Hey, you, go and wash that coal off your feet before you get into that—trough,' the night foreman would shout at a nigger. And at another nigger the night foreman would shout, 'Hey, you black sausage – don't you bloody well sweat so much, right into the kneading trough and all.'

For it is a characteristic of any person whose ancestors have lived in Africa for any length of time that he *does* sweat a lot. Whether he's a nigger, or a white Dutch-speaking Afrikaner, or a white English-speaking Jingo from Natal, if his forebears have resided in Africa for a couple of generations he sweats at the least provocation. Readers of Herodotus will recall that that great historian and geographer said the same thing about the Nubians of his time.

Because he was a simple soul, Jim Fish was, taken all in all, happy in his work. If he were asked by an American newspaper correspondent, or by an earnest inquirer delegated to the task by a UNO committee (UNO being in those days as much of an anachronism as nylons), Jim Fish would probably have confessed that he was deserving of one shilling and sixpence extra on a night when the bread-making machinery did not function as it should. The one shilling and sixpence would be to cover all that extra work he had in treading, Jim Fish would explain, marking time, left right, left right, to explain. And also to recompense him for all that trouble he took in cleaning himself, washing his legs and feet and toes in hot water. No, not when he got *into* the kneading trough. He never worried much about *that*, Jim Fish would declare, truthfully. It was when he had to get the sticky white dough off him afterwards. There was a job for you, now.

The real trouble about his job at the bakery, Jim Fish, alias Mletshwa Kusane, would confide to the correspondent of an American newspaper was the fact that it was nearly all night work. He didn't mind the pay so much. That was all right. Even after he had paid his rent and he had bought mealie-meal and goat's meat and such odds and ends of clothing as he needed, he was still able to save quite a bit, each month. This was a lot more than most white wage or salary earners were able to do, incidentally. All that happened to white people who worked for a boss was that they got deeper into debt, every month. Jim Fish would admit that he was saving, here in the city of Johannesburg. But he needed every penny he could scrape together. All the money he saved in Johannesburg had to go in lobola, when he got back to the kraal. Lobola was the money he had to pay some girl's father, so that he could get that girl as his wife. It wasn't any particular girl that Jim Fish was thinking about, of course. Practically any girl belonging to his tribe would do. As long as she could bear him children, and work for him, planting mealies and hoeing in the bean-fields, and bringing him a clay-pot full of beer when he called – him lying in the sun in front of the hut, and following the sun around. And maybe afterwards, if he came to Johannesburg again, and worked for the bakery for another season, he would even be able to buy a second wife, having enough money for another lobola. And then his children would be able to work for him, too, the children of his first and his second wife – and the children of his third wife, too, if he went to Johannesburg that often to make money to save up for a lobola. And who he would also have to work for him would be quite incidental children, that weren't his own, even, but that one or other of his wives begot by some other nigger man while he himself was in Johannesburg, working in the bakery.

That was a laugh on that other nigger man, all right.

It couldn't be too pleasant for that other nigger man, carrying on with Mletshwa's wives, and all that, in Mletshwa's absence, when what would happen out of it would be that that nigger man's children, by Mletshwa's wife, would end up by working for Mletshwa: tending his cattle for him, if they were boys; planting beans and kaffir-corn for him, if they were girls.

And if it turned out that the child that Mletshwa's wife conceived while Mletshwa was working in Johannesburg wasn't the child of another nigger man at all, but was the child of the white missionary at the Leboma mission station, then it would be a laugh on the white missionary, right enough. For that child would be lighter of skin than its brothers and sisters. Instead of its having a complexion like boot-polish, the missionary's child by Mletshwa's wife would be dark lemon in colour, with its hair less peperkorrel than the average negro's, and in the cast of its features there would be a couple of European traits. Consequently, that child would receive special privileges at the mission school and would be educated to be a school-teacher, or maybe even higher than a school-teacher, so that Mletshwa would be good for at least a pound a month from that child, whose education had cost him nothing. No wonder, therefore, that many a missionary walks about with an embittered look.

Late one night Mletshwa Kusane, alias Jim Fish, came away from the bakery with a deep sense of inner satisfaction. He felt he was somebody, and no mistake. For the mixing machine had broken down again. And this time he had been set to tread the dough in a confectionery trough. Not the dough for plebeian quartern loaves and twist loaves and standard brown loaves. But he had walked up and down, left right, left right, in a trough that had chilled eggs, even, mixed with the flour and water and yeast. Left right, left right, he was kneading, with his feet – brown on top and pinkish between the toes – the dough for slab cake and cream cakes and (with a few sultanas thrown in) for wedding cakes. The night foreman had noticed that, last time there was trouble with the mechanized equipment, Jim Fish had seemed to sweat somewhat less than the other niggers. And that was how Mletshwa got promoted to the confectionery trough. What the night foreman didn't notice was the effect that this unexpected promotion had on Mletshwa. Because he had been picked out for the unique honour of treading the dough in the confectionery container, Mletshwa suddenly started thinking that he was a king. A great king, he thought he was. And he started chanting in the Sechuana tongue a song that he had made up about himself, in the same way that any primitive African makes up a song about himself when he finds that, by chance, he is standing first in a line of pick-and-shovel labourers digging a ditch, or, if it's a gang of railway labourers moving a piece of track, and he happens to be walking in front.

And so that night, having been selected to tread the dough in the confectionery trough because he sweated less than other niggers, Mletshwa really let himself go. He felt no end proud of himself.

'Who is he, who is he, who is he?' Mletshwa chanted, going left right, left right, in double quick time,

'Who is he chosen by the Great White Man
To walk fast in the fine meal with the broken eggs in it?
Who is he but Mletshwa? –
Who is he but Mletshwa Kusane whose kraal is by the Malopo?

Who is he, the Mighty Trampling Elephant, elephant among elephants,
He with his feet washed clean in carbolic soap?
Who is the Mighty Elephant with his feet washed clean
With the thick white bubbles coming out of
The red carbolic soap – the White Man's red carbolic soap?
Who is he but Mletshwa Kusane whose kraal is by the Malopo?

Who is he that treads heavier than the rhinoceros –
The rhinoceros with his feet washed in the water from the White Man's faucet?
Who is he that treads with his feet washed cleaner than the White Man's feet?
Treading out white flour and yellow, stinking eggs and yeast
That is the beautiful food of the White Man?
Who is he but Mletshwa –
Who is he but Mletshwa Kusane whose kraal is by the Malopo?'

Inspired to unwonted exertions by his singing, Mletshwa was making a first-class job of treading that dough. When the night foreman looked again, Mletshwa was leaping up and down in the tub. One hand was raised up to the level of his shoulder, balancing an imaginary assegai. His other arm supported an equally imaginary raw-hide shield. What were not fictitious were the pieces of dough clinging to his working pants and shirt and even to one side of his neck. The night foreman was not a little surprised to see a nigger performing a Zulu war-dance in a kneading trough at that time of the night. Especially when those white splashes of dough could have passed as war-paint.

'None of that, Jim Fish,' the night foreman called out – impressed, in spite of himself, 'Get on with your work.'

One of the other Natives guffawed. But it *was* his work, this

Native thought. In prancing up and down like that, in the dough, Mletshwa was only doing his *work*. And here was the boss angry with Mletshwa about it. Surely, the ways of the White man were strange.

It was only a little later that the night foreman noticed what other effect the violent exercise had had on Jim Fish: he was sweating like a dozen niggers; the sweat was pouring off Mletshwa as though from a shower-bath. Which was something that Mletshwa had never had in his life – a shower – bath or any other kind of a bath.

This time the night foreman swore.

'Get out of that tub, you black son of a bitch,' he shouted. 'That's for cake for White people to eat, you bloody — Look at all the sweat running off your—backside into White people's cake.'

Mletshwa's was a temperament that was easily cowed. In a moment the sound of the night foreman's voice had changed him from a bloodthirsty warrior to a timid bushveld thing trying to escape from a trampling rhinoceros among rhinoceroses. In a split second he was out of the tub and halfway across the bakery floor towards his kaya in the back yard.

He had to return to the tub, however. The night foreman saw to that. The night foreman also saw to it that Mletshwa scraped all the dough off his feet and other parts of his person, and stuck it back where it belonged.

'Trying to make off with half the confectionery dough sticking to him,' the night foreman said to the mechanic who was working at the motor, working to get it started again. Then the night foreman addressed Mletshwa once more.

'Cha-cha,' he shouted. 'Inindaba wena want to steal wet meal, huh? Come on, put it all back. That lump between your toes, too. It's for the cake for White people to eat. You meningi skelm, you.'

Acknowledgements

'Makapan's Caves' first published in *Touleier* December 1930; reprinted in the collection *Mafeking Road* 1947. Copyright 1930 by H. C. Bosman.

'Yellow Moepels' first published in *South African Opinion* 25 January 1935; reprinted in the collection *Mafeking Road* 1947. Copyright 1935 by H. C. Bosman.

'The Red Coat', manuscript, Humanities Research Center, University of Austin, Texas; uncollected. Copyright © Mrs H. R. Lake, 1986.

'Unto Dust' first published in *Trek* February 1949; reprinted in the collection *Unto Dust* 1963. Copyright 1949 by H. C. Bosman.

'Funeral Earth' first published in *Vista* 1950; reprinted in the collection *Unto Dust* 1963. Copyright 1950 by H. C. Bosman.

'The Mafeking Road' first published in *South African Opinion* 23 August 1935; reprinted in the collection *Mafeking Road* 1947. Copyright 1935 by H. C. Bosman.

'Karel Flysman' first published in *African Magazine* June 1931; uncollected. Copyright 1931 by H. C. Bosman.

'The Question' first published in *Personality* 14 August 1969; uncollected. Copyright © Mrs H. R. Lake, 1969.

'The Rooinek' first published in *Touleier* January–February and March 1931; reprinted in the collection *Mafeking Road* 1947. Copyright 1931 by H. C. Bosman.

'Cometh Comet' first published in *Trek* June 1948; reprinted in the collection *Unto Dust* 1963. Copyright 1948 by H. C. Bosman.

'Ox-waggons on Trek' first published in *South African Opinion* 31 May 1935; reprinted in the collection *Mafeking Road* 1947. Copyright 1935 by H. C. Bosman.

'In the Withaak's Shade' first published in *South African Opinion* 22 March 1935; reprinted in the collection *Mafeking Road* 1947. Copyright 1935 by H. C. Bosman.

'A Boer Rip van Winkel' first published in the collection *Unto Dust* 1963. Copyright © Mrs H. R. Lake, 1963.

'In Church' first published in *Sjambok* 2 January 1931; uncollected. Copyright 1931 by H. C. Bosman.

'Secret Agent' first published in *Forum* 6 May 1950; uncollected. Copyright 1950 by H. C. Bosman.

'News Story' first published in *Forum* 10 June 1950; reprinted in the collection *A Bekkersdal Marathon* 1971. Copyright 1950 by H. C. Bosman.

'Lost City' first published in *Forum* 3 August 1951; reprinted in the collection *A Bekkersdal Marathon* 1971. Copyright 1951 by H. C. Bosman.

'Singular Events' first published in *Forum* 10 November 1950; uncollected. Copyright 1950 by H. C. Bosman.

'Detective Story' first published in *Forum* 18 May 1951; uncollected. Copyright 1951 by H. C. Bosman.

'At This Time of Year' first published in *Forum* 15 December 1950; uncollected. Copyright 1950 by H. C. Bosman.

'A Bekkersdal Marathon' first published in *Forum* 22 April 1950; reprinted in the collection *A Bekkersdal Marathon* 1971. Copyright 1950 by H. C. Bosman.

'Laugh, Clown, Laugh' first published in *Forum* 12 January 1951; reprinted in the collection *Jurie Steyn's Post Office* 1971. Copyright 1951 by H. C. Bosman.

'Play within a Play' first published in *Forum* 19 August 1950; reprinted in the collection *A Bekkersdal Marathon* 1971. Copyright 1950 by H. C. Bosman.

'Birth Certificate' first published in *Forum* 12 August 1950; reprinted in the collection *A Bekkersdal Marathon* 1971. Copyright 1950 by H. C. Bosman.

'White Ant' first published in *Forum* 8 July 1950; reprinted in the collection *Jurie Steyn's Post Office* 1971. Copyright 1950 by H. C. Bosman.

'Day of Wrath' first published in *Forum* 26 January 1951; reprinted in the collection *Jurie Steyn's Post Office* 1971. Copyright 1951 by H. C. Bosman.

'Jim Fish', manuscript, Humanities Research Center, University of Austin, Texas; first published in the collection *Selected Stories* 1980. Copyright © Mrs H. R. Lake, 1980.